AUSTRALIA'S
MOST
DANGEROUS

Red-back spider *(Latrodectus hasselti).*

AUSTRALIA'S
MOST
DANGEROUS

spiders, snakes and marine creatures

IDENTIFICATION AND FIRST AID

Text by Julian White, Carl Edmonds
and Paul Zborowski

AUSTRALIAN GEOGRAPHIC

Published by Australian Geographic Pty Ltd
PO Box 321, Terrey Hills NSW 2084, Australia
Phone: (02) 9450 2344. Fax: (02) 9450 2990
email: books@ausgeo.com.au

First published 1998; reprinted 2001

Managing Director: Ken Rosebery
Production/Creative Director: Tony Gordon
Managing Editor, Books: Averil Moffat

Managing Editor: Bill Templeman
Editor: Geordie Torr
Design: Bruno Grasswill
Production Manager: Valerie Reed
Copy Editors: Frank Povah, Mary Halbmeyer
Photo Research: Lydia Koster
Editorial Assistants: Joanne Diver, Susan McCreery, Sandy Richardson

Printed in Hong Kong by Dai Nippon Printing

National Library of Australia Cataloguing-in-Publication Data:
      Zborowski, Paul, 1955 – .
      Australia's most dangerous spiders, snakes and sea creatures:
      Australian Geographic field guide.
      Includes index.
      ISBN 1 86276 023 3.
1. Poisonous arachnida – Australia. 2. Poisonous snakes – Australia. 3. Dangerous aquatic
animals – Australia. 4. Dangerous animals – Australia. I. Edmonds, Carl. II. White, Julian. III.
Australian Geographic Pty Ltd. IV. Title.
      591.650994

Acknowledgements
For their assistance with this book, Australian Geographic thanks: Peter Arnold, Kevin
Broady, Barry Bruce, Rob Fearon, Bryan Fry, Michael Guinea, Peter Harlow, Wayne Hodgson,
Jeff Johnson, Nicki Kenvyn, Peter Last, Bruce Livett, Jonathan Majer, Charlie Manolis,
Loisette Marsh, St John Ambulance Australia, Jamie Seymour, Rod Simpson, Courtenay
Smithers, John Stevens, Tim Stranks, Clive Wilkinson, Steve Wilson.

CONTENTS

Blue-ringed octopus (*Hapalochlaena maculosa*).

Foreword

The sort of hysteria that surrounds venomous and other dangerous Australian animals is a bit lost on me. I was brought up on Sydney's north shore, where funnel-web and red-back spiders, red-bellied blacks and many other venomous snakes were the norm, and like most kids who live near bushland, I was taught to be cautious of snakes and spiders. In my case, caution soon gave way to curiosity.

I started to develop an interest in herpetology (the study of reptiles and amphibians) at the age of 12, with my own lizard pit in my backyard. At the time – the mid-1950s – I was the youngest person to apply for membership of the Australian Reptile Club (now the Australian Herpetological Society). My mentor was the renowned David McPhee, who was the club's president.

I once turned up at David's place with a jam-jar full of funnel-web spiders – there must have been about a dozen. My mother knew nothing of this and I'm sure she wouldn't have been impressed if she had. David didn't know what to do with them and called the Commonwealth Serum Laboratories. They said they'd send him some small containers to put them in but they didn't arrive for three weeks, by which time there was only one very fat spider left.

Venomous snakes, dangerous marine animals and other potentially hazardous creatures such as crocodiles are a part of Australia's wonderful natural heritage, and the humans who've lived with these animals the longest – Australia's indigenous peoples – accept them with ease. Many of the people who've come to this land in more recent times have left relatively benign countries such as England, which has only one venomous snake. No wonder they start their lives here with quite a fear.

Once you learn to put that fear aside, you can appreciate these "dangerous" animals for what they really are – magnificent predators, superbly adapted to quickly subdue prey or defend themselves against aggressors. And even if you can't bring yourself to stop and watch a snake or spider instead of running away from it, try to remember that these creatures are quite sensible. Given the chance, they'll head off in the other direction rather than confront a human.

Dick Smith
CHAIRMAN, AUSTRALIAN GEOGRAPHIC SOCIETY

INTRODUCTION

Australia is home to many of the world's most dangerous and venomous creatures. Unfortunately for some Australians and many visitors from overseas, fear of these creatures can dampen their enjoyment of our wonderful natural environment. Often this fear is the product of misinformation and a lack of knowledge and it's our hope that by raising awareness of our potentially dangerous animals, this book will dispel some of that fear and foster an appreciation of these fascinating creatures.

The book is divided into four chapters – covering snakes, spiders and insects, marine creatures, and first aid – each written by a recognised expert in their field. The animals featured are described in detail, with colour photographs and distribution maps to aid identification. As well as enabling the reader to accurately identify Australia's most dangerous and venomous creatures, these chapters also provide interesting insights into their biology and information on the types of injuries they can cause. *Australia's Most Dangerous* provides the scientific names of all the animals described because of the wide regional variation and inconsistencies in common names – a name in general use in one part of the country may mean nothing, or even refer to a different species, in another area.

The book's final chapter contains expert advice on the first aid and medical treatment required in the unlikely event that someone is bitten or stung – information that could save a life. Written by a specialist marine medical practitioner and a clinical toxinologist, with additional information and illustrative references provided by St John Ambulance Australia, it's an invaluable source of vital information on the nature and treatment of injuries caused by dangerous and venomous animals.

Each of the animals described in this book, while potentially dangerous, has a fascinating ecological story to tell. Sculpted by evolution's slow hand, most are highly efficient predators and have an important role to play within the ecosystems of which they are a part. By learning to look past their hazardous attributes, we can begin to appreciate their beauty and to recognise their ecological importance.

The dangers associated with these organisms are usually exaggerated – most won't bite or sting unless harassed – and being able to recognise potentially dangerous animals and taking a few sensible precautions, such as those detailed within, will reduce what small risks these creatures present to us. Armed with the knowledge contained in this book, the reader will hopefully develop an appreciation of these remarkable creatures, more deserving of our respect than our fear.

Using scientific names

They may seem complex and enigmatic but scientific or "Latin" names are given to organisms according to a set of relatively simple rules. The classification system currently used – the binominal system – gives each species a name made up of two parts, the first part indicating the genus to which the organism belongs, and the second designating the species. The whole name is written in italics, with the first letter of the generic name a capital letter and the specific name all in lower case (e.g. *Notechis scutatus*, the common tiger snake). When more than one species of the same genus is listed, the name of the genus is abbreviated to its first letter after the first mention (e.g. *Notechis scutatus*, *N. ater*). Subspecies – variants of species that are not different enough to warrant full species status – are given a third name (e.g. *Notechis ater niger*, a subspecies of the black tiger snake).

When an organism's genus is known but the species is unclear, the generic name appears followed by the abbreviation sp. (e.g. *Notechis* sp. refers to a species of the tiger snake). When referring generally to a number of species in a particular genus, the generic name appears followed by the abbreviation spp. (e.g. *Notechis* spp. refers to several species of tiger snake).

Species are grouped into a series of progressively larger collections. Closely related species are grouped together in a genus (plural: genera), genera are grouped into families, families into orders, orders into classes and classes into phyla (singular: phylum).

STEVE WILSON

Death adders are easily recognised by their short fat body, broad triangular head and slender tail. Holding their tail-tip close to their snout, as this common death adder is doing, they wriggle it convulsively to lure prey within striking range.

Chapter one

VENOMOUS SNAKES

Dr JULIAN WHITE

Snakes in general, and venomous snakes in particular, are almost universally feared or loathed in Western societies, emotions no doubt further fuelled when the Hebrew story of the serpent in the Garden of Eden was introduced with Christianity into Europe. Yet in many societies snakes are far from despised; indeed they are sometimes revered. But in all societies, venomous snakes are treated with caution, and for good reason. Snake venoms contain a bewildering array of toxic substances, many of which are more than capable of killing an adult human.

Snakebite is a significant problem around the world, especially in the rural tropics. It's now generally agreed that at least 50,000 people die each year from snakebite, though some experts believe that the number could be as high or higher than 100,000. Certainly more than a million people worldwide suffer at least some ill effects from snakebite every year, and in many areas the numbers are increasing. It's been suggested that with increasing urbanisation snake numbers, and therefore snakebites, will decrease. However, the latest evidence from Africa and South America suggests the opposite, so the problem doesn't seem likely to disappear at any time in the near future.

Despite the toll extracted by snakes, it isn't fair to say that their impact on our society is uniformly negative. For example, they are important predators of major pest species, particularly mice and rats, which would undoubtedly cause far more human suffering without snakes keeping their numbers in check. Indeed farmers in some countries, the USA and India among them, have recognised this and protect and encourage snakes on their farms, thereby reducing losses caused by rodent damage to stored grain and other produce. On Australian banana plantations, it's not unusual to see large carpet pythons living in packing sheds; an effective deterrent to four-footed pests. And strange as it may seem, snake venoms are also benefiting humankind. Long utilised in natural remedies and in Eastern medicine, they are now being used in Western biomedical research. Because snake venoms contain numerous components, each with highly specific effects on the human body, they are extremely useful in medical research. For instance, snake neurotoxins (page 19), have helped us to understand the way in which nerves work and have been used in research on nerve diseases such as myasthenia gravis. Drugs derived from snake venoms include pain relievers and a substance for inhibiting the formation of blood clots. With a wealth of other potential benefits awaiting discovery, venomous snakes undoubtedly return humankind far more than they take by accidental envenomation.

VENOMOUS SNAKE BIOLOGY

Worldwide, there is a surprising diversity of venomous snake species, possessing a range of different venoms and methods for delivering them. Although all venoms have evolved from saliva, they have very different effects, acting on different body systems.

By a quirk of history, the vast majority of Australia's snakes are venomous, at least to some degree. They almost all belong to the family Elapidae, which also includes the cobras, mambas and coral snakes. The elapids were among the first snakes to arrive in Australia, probably coming in from Asia about 20–15 million years ago (mya). They diversified quickly, filling most of the available niches, so that by the time humans arrived, thought to be about 60,000 years ago, they found a continent inhabited by some of the world's most deadly species.

The high proportion of deadly snakes in Australia has led to a perception of the dangers of snakebite that is verging on mythological. Yet in reality the risks are quite small. The populations of most snakes are sparse and a snake will usually move away at the approach of a human so it's rare indeed to come across one while walking in the bush. There are also many simple precautions that we can all take to reduce the possibility of being bitten by a venomous snake.

The types of venomous snakes

There are six major families of venomous snakes in the world, four of which are found in Australia.

The family Colubridae is found worldwide (page 14, top), but in Australia is confined to northern and eastern regions. Most colubrid snakes are non-venomous and few possess fangs. Even fewer are capable of serious harm to

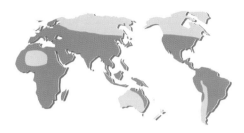

World distribution of colubrid snakes. Family Colubridae

humans and none of the Australian species is regarded as dangerous. Our only significantly venomous colubrid, the brown tree snake (*Boiga irregularis*), has the typical "back fangs" of the venomous members of this family. Although the species can be aggressive, its venom is relatively weak and the placement of its fangs at the rear of the mouth reduces the likelihood of serious envenomation; no serious bites to humans having been reported in Australia. However, this species has been accidentally introduced to some Pacific islands, notably Guam, where the absence of predators has led to a population explosion, which has in turn led to dramatic bird extinctions and frequent bites. Some infants have experienced severe effects, but, again, no deaths have been recorded.

The family Elapidae also occurs worldwide (below), with the greatest diversity of species in Australia, where elapids are the dominant snake fauna.

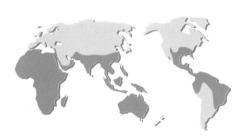

World distribution of elapid snakes. Family Elapidae

All have small- to medium-sized fangs at the front of the mouth and while all species are venomous, most are either too small or have venom too weak to injure humans.

There are about 25 species of land-dwelling snakes classified as potentially deadly in Australia – these include some of the world's most dangerous snakes – and they are discussed in detail in the following section. All are members of the family Elapidae.

The sea-snakes are also now considered to belong to the family Elapidae – within the subfamily Hydrophiinae. They are a diverse group, distributed throughout the Indian and Pacific oceans (left), especially in the coastal waters of

World distribution of sea-snakes. Subfamily Hydrophiinae

warmer areas. Like the other elapids, they have front fangs and highly toxic venoms. Sea-snakes are discussed under "Other venomous marine animals", on page 144.

Comparatively poorly known, the side-fanged vipers of the family Atractaspididae are confined to Africa and the Middle East (right, above). They have distinctive venoms that have been the subject of intense study in recent years.

World distribution of side-fanged vipers. Family Atractaspididae

The last family of venomous snakes, the Viperidae (vipers and pit-vipers) is widely distributed, occurring almost everywhere except Australia and New Guinea (right, below). The very long fangs of these snakes are carried at the front of the mouth and are hinged, folding to lie

World distribution of vipers and pit vipers. Family Viperidae

along the roof of the mouth when it's closed and rotating forward during a strike. Though their venoms are generally less toxic than those of the elapid snakes, they often deliver larger amounts. Common in the rural tropics, they are the leading cause of snakebite death and injury in many countries.

Snake fangs

Snake fangs have evolved from ordinary teeth to become superb instruments for delivering venom into prey. Paired one on each side of the mouth in the upper jaw, fangs vary in length from a millimetre or less to more than 3 centimetres, and in most have special channels that deliver the venom near the tip. If one is lost there is usually a reserve already growing, ready to take its place.

Snakes have many non-fang teeth as well, which may also leave marks when they bite. Most people think that a bite from a venomous snake will leave a pair of obvious puncture marks and while this is often true, other bite

MURRAY FREDERICK

THE THREE MAJOR TYPES OF SNAKE FANGS
**Venomous colubrid snakes (left) have small fangs positioned at the
rear of the mouth. The fangs of elapid snakes (centre) are also
relatively small but are placed at the front of the mouth. Vipers
(right) have medium to very large fangs that are mounted on a
hinged bone, folding against the roof of the mouth when not in use.**

patterns are also commonly seen: a single fang may puncture the skin, or the
snake may pull away, leaving scratches rather than punctures. Small fangs
may leave only the tiniest of puncture marks, difficult to see with the naked
eye. The three major types of snake fang are shown above.

Snake venom

Why do snakes have venom?

Snakes use their venom primarily to help them feed. Many of the animals they
eat, such as rats and mice, move quickly and some can put up a fight,
potentially injuring the snake in the process. Its venom allows the snake to
quickly inflict a fatal blow, some species holding onto the prey until it
succumbs while others retreat to await its victim's death, using its superb
sense of smell to locate the dying prey. Many different toxins can cause rapid
death and most snake venoms contain several types, just for good measure.

Snakes also use their venoms in the digestion process. Like other reptiles,
snakes are cold-blooded, or ectothermic, meaning that they must use an
external heat source to achieve their desired body temperature. Although this
makes them more energy-efficient – unlike warm-blooded (endothermic)
animals such as humans, they don't waste a large part of their energy just
keeping warm – it does have some disadvantages.

To digest food, most enzymes in the stomach and gut need to be above a
certain temperature, so if the snake gets too cold, digestion stops and the food
starts to rot and must be regurgitated. Evolved from salivary glands, venom is
often very effective at speeding up the breakdown of food, with many venom
components related to digestive enzymes. This is probably a real advantage

to venomous snakes, though the many species of non-venomous snakes seem to manage quite well without this "super charging" of the digestive process.

The last major use of snake venom is as a defence. Some snakes, such as the American coral snakes, have warning colouration that advertises their venomous nature, while others employ impressive threat displays. Best known of these are the cobras, with their flared neck and hissing associated with mock strikes. If these warnings aren't effective, a highly toxic bite will serve to dissuade a potential predator.

Composition of venoms

Snake venoms are made in specialised glands that are generally positioned above the upper jaw towards the back of the snake's head (below). Nearly all snake venoms consist of a complex mixture of substances, rather than just a single toxin. Each toxin may have one or more distinct actions and several toxins may combine to exert interactive effects. Snake venoms evolve rapidly, allowing for great diversity. Studies in Australia have shown that venoms of

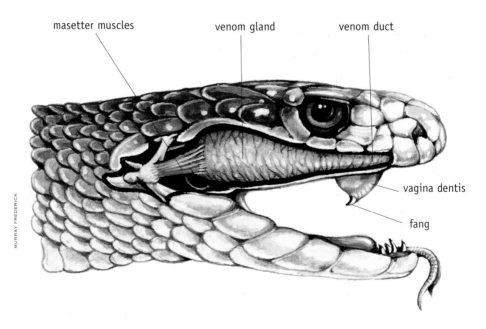

VENOM DELIVERY SYSTEM OF AN ELAPID SNAKE
When a venomous snake bites its prey, the masseter muscles contract, squeezing the venom gland and forcing venom through the venom duct, down through the fang and into the victim. The vagina dentis is a protective sheath that slides up the fang as it enters the prey.

isolated tiger snake populations change in only a few thousand years or less and though effective components are usually preserved, the snakes are continually "experimenting" with new toxins. The genetic basis for this can be likened to the system by which humans produce a wide and ever-changing variety of antibodies to fight infection.

Venom is produced in the venom gland, where it's stored until needed. When a snake strikes, muscles contract around the gland, compressing it and forcing the venom out through a duct, along the channel in the fang and into the victim. Snakes can control the amount of venom they inject when they bite but this also depends on the type of snake, how big it is, and how recently it last used its venom. Venom production is measured when snakes are "milked", that is, made to release venom through the fangs into a container. The venom is then dried and it's the dry weight that is usually reported.

We measure how dangerous venom is by applying toxicity tests, the most common being a test called an LD50, which measures the toxicity of the complete venom. The name means "lethal dose 50 per cent", or that dose of venom that will kill half of all the designated test animals, usually mice. Unfortunately, this means killing quite a large number of mice and researchers are trying to design new tests to replace the LD50.

We often hear that Australia has the world's deadliest snakes and if we look carefully at venom LD50 tests this appears true enough – many of our snakes do have extremely toxic venom. However, deadliness isn't just a question of venom toxicity, but how much venom is delivered, how likely the snake is to bite, and how frequently its bites are likely to occur. The most toxic of all snake venoms is that of Australia's inland taipan, yet there are few recorded bites for this species and while most of these have been severe, none have resulted in death.

In contrast, the carpet vipers of Africa have a far less toxic venom but are abundant near human habitation and bites are common, resulting in many thousands of deaths each year. However, poor treatment facilities, compared to those available in Australia, certainly contribute to the high incidence of fatalities.

Because snake venoms are complex mixtures of components with varying and sometimes multiple actions, they've been classified in a number of ways. In general, the most useful classification is based on their effects on humans and it's this system I've opted to use here.

Neurotoxins

Neurotoxins cause paralysis by acting on the nerves. There are a variety of snake neurotoxins, working in different ways, that cause paralysis. The most important medically act at the "neuromuscular junction", the end of the chain of nerves that delivers messages from the brain to muscle cells, telling them to contract. They work by blocking the signal between the nerve ending and the muscle, which is relayed by a chemical called a neurotransmitter. The toxins act on both voluntary and respiratory muscles, so a severely affected person can neither move nor breathe.

Venoms that block the release of the neurotransmitter from the nerve cell are known as presynaptic neurotoxins, while those that prevent the muscle cell from receiving the message to contract are called postsynaptic neurotoxins. The former are the most powerful paralysing toxins and are found particularly in the venom of taipans and tiger snakes. Because these toxins damage the nerve, antivenom is not very effective at reversing its effects, and if fully paralysed in this way a person may require a machine to help them breathe for days, weeks or even months. The postsynaptic neurotoxins are more common, but less powerful, and they can be neutralised and the paralysis reversed by antivenom. Snakes producing this sort of venom include the death adder.

Myotoxins

Muscle cells are also targeted by a group of toxins called myotoxins, which cause them to dissolve and release their contents into the blood. Myotoxins start damaging the muscle cells within an hour or so of an effective bite and affected muscle cells are largely destroyed within 24 hours. As a result, the kidneys may fail, the heart may stop and the urine is turned red by a muscle pigment called myoglobin. Muscle destruction (myolysis) is a common effect of tiger and mulga snake bites.

Procoagulants and anticoagulants

Both of these toxins act against the clotting action of the blood. Procoagulants destroy the clotting protein whereas anticoagulants block the clotting process and are generally much less dangerous than the procoagulant venoms. However, both types put the victim at risk of severe bleeding. Procoagulants are especially common in the venom of brown snakes, tiger snakes and taipans and are a common cause of death from snakebite. Anticoagulants are found in the venom of mulga snakes and some related species.

Effects of snakebite on humans

How common is snakebite?

In Australia, we take a certain morbid pride in the deadliness of our snakes and many people are under the impression that snakebite is common and deaths frequent. Fortunately this isn't the case. There have been up to 3000 cases of snakebite recorded in Australia in one year, but the annual figure is usually much lower – and of these, only a few hundred are severe enough to need antivenom treatment. Over the past 20 years there have been, on average, only two deaths per year from snakebite and examination of these cases suggests that some could have been avoided if correct first aid had been used. So the chance of dying from snakebite in Australia is low, due in part to our extensive and well-equipped hospital system and our good antivenoms.

Most snakebite victims are adults, with children accounting for only about 25 per cent of bites, although their smaller size means they are more likely to develop severe symptoms. Snakebite can occur at any time of year, but is more common in the warmer months and though more bites happen in the country than in big cities, city dwellers are not exempt.

There are well-established snake-catching groups in many cities and towns and their experience shows that some snakes are common in urban areas. In Adelaide, for example, hundreds of venomous snakes are caught each year, and 11 per cent of all captures are inside a home, so there is good reason for every Australian to know how to avoid snakes and how to give first aid for snakebite (page 169). Though statistics are still too limited to allow certainty, it appears that these snake-catching services may be reducing the number of bites in urban areas. Support your local snake-catcher!

How often is a snakebite severe?

The severity of a snakebite depends on the type of snake. Brown snakes, having adapted well to human environments, are common and hence responsible for the greatest number of snakebites and snakebite deaths. However, fewer than 25 per cent of brown snake bites are severe; the rest being either very minor or "dry bites", where the snake fails to inject venom.

At the other end of the scale is the taipan, which nearly always delivers a potentially fatal bite. Indeed, before a taipan antivenom was developed, only two people were known to have survived bites. This is one reason why some people consider the taipan the deadliest snake in the world.

Of course, in any case of snakebite it's impossible to be sure just how severe the bite is, so every incident should be treated as severe and correct first aid promptly applied.

✚ **For detailed first aid see page 169.**

Prevention of snakebite

Although snakebite treatment is now very effective, it's of course better not to be bitten at all. Commonsense and care are the basic ingredients in avoiding snakebite and it's worth noting that very few experienced, careful bushwalkers are bitten by snakes, but plenty who ignore safety are. The following advice may help you avoid a bite when you're walking in bushland areas or, if you are bitten, to survive.

● Never bushwalk alone: who'll help if you are bitten?
● Wear appropriate footwear and clothing to reduce the amount of bare skin around the feet, ankles and lower legs and hence the chance of an effective bite.
● Look where you walk. Don't step over obstructions such as fallen logs without checking what's on the other side.
● Don't run in long grass or other thick vegetation where you can't see what lies ahead. Remember that you can outrun a snake, so by running you may deny it the chance to get out of your way.
● Be especially vigilant in and around water, often a favourite haunt of snakes.
● Take an appropriate first-aid kit with you, just in case. You can rig a splint from a branch, but bandages don't grow on bushes. Take several bandages with you, preferably of the elastic type; one won't be enough to bind a whole leg.
● Let someone know where you're going and when you plan to return.
● Make sure that you know snakebite first aid and have enough bandages.
● If you find a snake close by, don't try to kill it. Seek expert advice and assistance, either from a local snake-catcher or your State wildlife authority.

● If you have snakes around your house from time to time, there are several things you can do to discourage them:

- Remove rubbish that might harbour prey, such as small lizards or mice, or provide shelter for snakes. Corrugated iron stacked on the ground makes a popular snake haven so remove it or stack sheets vertically.

- In hot, dry weather, open containers of water may attract snakes; if this happens, make the water less accessible.

- If snakes are coming close to the house, make sure that they can't get in by keeping doors fully closed and sealing any gaps.

Although most snakes will move away from an approaching human it's always worth taking a few simple precautions when bushwalking. Wear appropriate footwear, look where you walk and carry a constrictive bandage.

Part I I

VENOMOUS SNAKE IDENTIFICATION

Accurately identifying the different species of dangerous Australian snakes usually involves using a combination of colour pattern, distribution and scale characteristics. The table of scale patterns that appears on page 53, when used with the photographs and distribution maps provided, should make it possible to identify the snakes mentioned in this book. The table isn't meant to be exhaustive, however, and anyone who would like more detailed information on the identification of Australian snakes should consult Harold Cogger's *Reptiles and Amphibians of Australia*.

Scales are a very useful snake identification tool because most species have a unique combination of scale patterns. For example, the shape and number of scales on the head and the number of scale rows in the mid-body area differs from species to species. Similarly, certain scales have divided in two during the evolution of some species. All of these characteristics are remarkably consistent among members of the same species. Clearly, using the information provided here will require a close examination of the snake, because scale characteristics won't be plain from a distance, but it's advisable to avoid handling venomous snakes and unless you have experience with these animals, this information should only be used for identifying dead specimens.

The first step in identifying a snake is to determine which species inhabit the area in which it was found – for this you should use the distribution maps and distribution information in this section. You should then be able to narrow down the possibilities using the photographs. Finally, by comparing the scale characteristics of your snake with those of the likely species it should be possible to identify the specimen.

The information included here can also be used to determine the snake species from which a shed skin has come. A complete skin holds a "map" of the scales of the snake to which it once belonged, right down to those that covered the eyes.

Brown snakes

Dangerous species: *Pseudonaja textilis* (eastern or common brown snake), *P. nuchalis* (western brown snake or gwardar), *P. affinis* (dugite), *P. inframacula* (peninsula brown snake), *P. guttata* (spotted brown snake), *P. ingrami* (Ingram's brown snake).

Distribution: Widely distributed across mainland Australia in most habitats, though relatively uncommon in alpine regions. The eastern brown snake is found across most of the eastern half of Australia with isolated populations in the Northern Territory, while the western brown snake occurs virtually Australia-wide with the exception of a narrow strip around the southern and eastern coasts. The dugite is restricted to south-western Western Australia and a narrow coastal band extending as far as Eyre Peninsula in South Australia and the peninsula brown snake is restricted to Eyre Peninsula. The spotted brown snake is distributed in a wide band through central and western Queensland into the NT. Ingram's brown snake is found in a band from central NT into western Queensland.

Western brown

Eastern brown

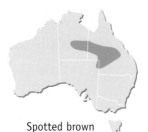

Spotted brown

Ingram's brown

Dugite

Peninsula brown

Brown snakes are highly variable in colour. Even within a single clutch of eggs, hatchlings may show a diversity of colour and pattern. Adults may be any shade of brown, through to grey, almost black, orange or dark yellow. They may be speckled, have prominent dark bands, or dark head scales. Most brown snakes have pale belly (ventral) scales, often speckled with orange. Juvenile colour patterns are equally diverse, although they all have a dark head and a dark band on the neck.

STEVE WILSON

The eastern brown snake is normally shy, becoming nervous and aggressive only if provoked. Abundant in open forest and farmlands of eastern Australia, this species has probably benefited from land clearing and the introduction of the house mouse.

Brown snakes generally hunt during the day, becoming nocturnal in hot weather. They are opportunistic feeders, preying on whatever is available to them, especially small mammals and reptiles. In agricultural areas they are often important predators of house mice. Despite having an extremely toxic venom, brown snakes will sometimes also subdue their prey by constriction. They have adapted very well to human encroachment and are common in urban areas, where they frequently shelter under things like stacked timber and corrugated iron.

Perhaps because they've adapted so well to human environments, brown snakes are the leading cause of snakebite in Australia and account for more deaths than any other type of snake. The threat display is spectacular – mouth agape, forebody raised off the ground in an S-shape, frequent rapid strikes – and is the source of the brown snakes' generic name: *Pseudonaja* means false cobra. All species have very potent venoms and the eastern brown snake has the second most potent land-snake venom in the world, second only to the

One of our most widespread snake species, the western brown snake comes in a bewildering array of colours and patterns. Some colour forms may actually represent distinct species.

inland taipan. All brown snakes are egg layers, producing an average of 6–16 eggs per clutch.

Fortunately, perhaps because their fangs are small and only relatively small amounts of venom are produced, brown snake bites are frequently "dry", and no venom is injected – perhaps fewer than one in four requiring antivenom. Even before antivenom became available, less than 10 per cent of brown snake bites proved fatal. Of course, when bitten you can't be sure whether you'll be in the lucky majority or the unlucky minority, so every bite should be treated as potentially serious.

Bites from the small fangs are easily missed because they can be hard to see and local pain is uncommon and it's possible to be bitten by a brown snake while walking through long grass, yet be quite unaware of the fact, even when a lethal amount of venom has been injected.

Brown snake envenomation can cause bleeding, kidney damage and paralysis, although the latter is rare. The antivenom is very effective, though many ampoules are often needed.

Ingram's (above) and spotted brown snakes (below) are poorly known specialised species confined to tropical grasslands on deeply cracking claypans. They are both nocturnal, hiding by day in the soil cracks.

27

Tiger snakes

Dangerous species: *Notechis scutatus* (common or eastern tiger snake), *N. ater* (black tiger snake), *N. occidentalis* (western tiger snake or norne).

Distribution: Found in cooler, wetter areas of southern and eastern Australia, including Tasmania and some of the islands off the southern coast. The common tiger snake is usually found near watercourses or wetlands from south-eastern Queensland to the south-eastern corner of SA. Black tiger snakes are restricted to Tasmania, islands in Bass Strait and off the SA coast, and restricted areas of mainland SA. The western tiger snake is restricted to the south-western corner of WA.

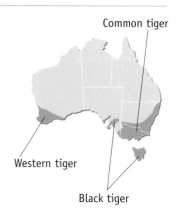

Common tiger

Western tiger

Black tiger

Typical common tiger snakes are grey, blue-grey or brown above, with distinct paler – often yellowish – bands, and pale belly scales. However, unbanded brown forms that are sometimes mistaken for brown snakes do occur. Black tiger snakes come in a variety of subspecies, each restricted to a particular area, sometimes a single island. They are usually black all over, though juveniles may have thin yellow bands.

Identification of species or subspecies may be difficult, but can often be determined by geographic location. The differences between the species or subspecies have clinical significance because the varying toxicity and venom quantity will influence the dosage of antivenom.

Tiger snakes are usually diurnal and feed predominantly on animals in and near water such as frogs. The tiger snakes that live on offshore islands are an exception to this rule. These animals feed on seabird chicks but they face a problem: the birds reproduce seasonally and the chicks quickly grow too large for the snakes to eat. The snakes solve this by gorging themselves for a short period and then fasting for the rest of the year. It's only the snakes' low metabolism, and hence low energy demands, that allows them to exploit this fleeting resource. Tiger snakes produce live young and litters of over 100 have been recorded, although typically the number will be closer to 20.

The tiger snake undoubtedly gained its name from its banded colouration and perhaps from its occasionally pugnacious nature. Tiger snake bites are

The black tiger snakes (above) found on Chappell Island in Bass Strait are larger than their mainland counterparts. Their size and low energy needs allow them to survive by exploiting the brief glut of fat muttonbird chicks. The western tiger snake (below) enjoys a broader diet of frogs, lizards and mammals.

STEVE WILSON

Common tiger snakes live along creekbanks, in swamps and in the cool moist forests of south-eastern Australia. During floods hundreds may aggregate in bushes or on high ground.

among the most common and unpleasant of all Australian snakebites. Before an antivenom was developed in the 1930s, nearly 50 per cent of all people bitten by tiger snakes died, either from paralysis or other problems such as bleeding, muscle damage or kidney failure. Tiger snake bites remain the second most common cause of snakebite death in Australia, though this probably amounts to only one fatality or less per year.

Tiger snake venom is one of the most toxic of all snake venoms and is produced in moderate quantities. Tiger snake antivenom is quite effective at neutralising most of the venom's deadly effects, but by the time effects such as muscle damage are evident, it may be too late to reverse them. Because of this, it's important to administer the antivenom as soon as major effects become obvious.

Copperheads

Dangerous species: *Austrelaps superbus* (lowland or common copperhead), *A. ramsayi* (highland copperhead), *A. labialis* (pygmy copperhead).

Distribution: Restricted to cooler parts of south-eastern Australia. The lowland copperhead occurs in eastern and northern Tasmania and from south-eastern SA across most of southern Victoria, almost to the New South Wales border in places. The highland copperhead is found in cool to cold regions of the Great Dividing Range from northern Victoria almost to Queensland. The pygmy copperhead is restricted to Kangaroo Island, SA, and in a limited area in the Mt Lofty Ranges near Adelaide.

Lowland copperhead

Pygmy copperhead

Highland copperhead

Until recently, the lowland copperhead was regarded as the only species – the highland and pygmy species were considered variants or subspecies. The body colour of the lowland copperhead is generally reddish brown to grey, occasionally almost black, grading to a distinctive orange to red colour on the lateral scales. This grades to cream on the belly scales. The pale edging on the front portions of the scales on upper and lower lips is diffuse, and the rest of the head is darker, sometimes with a coppery sheen. The pale edging of the lip scales is common to all three species and distinguishes their genus among dangerous Australian snakes. The highland copperhead has similar colouration to the lowland species although the colour is usually darker and the lip markings more prominent. The pygmy variety is grey to olive-grey in body colour, grading to pale colours laterally, and with prominently barred lips.

The pygmy copperhead is usually slender, in contrast to the lowland and highland copperheads, which are more robust. The lowland copperhead may reach 1.25 metres in length on the mainland, but on some Bass Strait islands specimens may grow to 1.7 m. Highland copperheads are smaller, reaching only 1.1 m in length, while pygmy copperheads are rarely over 0.8 m long.

All copperheads are found in cool to cold, generally moist areas; they are

Lowland (above) and highland copperheads (below) can thrive in cool southern and high-elevation habitats because their dark colours soak up the sun's heat and their stocky bodies help retain it. Producing live young, rather than eggs, may also be an adaptation to the cold climates in which they live.

among Australia's most cool-adapted snakes, sometimes seen basking while there's still snow around them. Adults of all three species feed principally on frogs, while juveniles eat mostly small lizards. The lowland copperhead has a reputation for eating other snakes. They all forage during the day, though they may be active after dusk on hot nights. Tussock grasses are favoured both for foraging and shelter. All give birth to fully formed young, up to 45 per litter (although usually fewer), from January to March.

Though copperheads are relatively common, bites are few, perhaps because they are infrequently encountered and often reluctant to bite. As a result, very little is known about the effect of their venom on humans and only the venom of the lowland copperhead has been studied in any detail. A few fatalities have occurred, apparently due to paralysis. Bites may cause paralysis, muscle damage and mild bleeding. Tiger snake antivenom is generally considered appropriate for major copperhead envenomation, though documentation of its effectiveness is scant. Of nearly a dozen recorded bites by the pygmy copperhead, none have proved severe. In general, however, all copperheads should be considered potentially dangerous.

Rough-scaled snake

Dangerous species: *Tropidechis carinatus* (rough-scaled snake, Clarence River tiger snake).
Distribution: Occurs in two widely separated areas; the coast and ranges of north-eastern NSW and south-eastern Queensland from around Barrington Tops to Fraser Island, and in the wet tropics of north-eastern Queensland.

Rough-scaled snakes are quite variable in colour: usually dark brown to olive-brown above, with most specimens exhibiting distinct narrow dark bands. The lips and belly are generally cream coloured. This snake grows up to 1 m in length and may be confused with the harmless keelback (*Tropidonophis mairii*) from which it differs in lacking a loreal scale (the scale between the nasal scale and the preocular scale) and having undivided subcaudal scales.

Generally found near watercourses or swamps or in rainforests, the rough-

The rough-scaled snake is named for the raised ridge or keel on each of its scales. Though usually seen on the ground, it is a skilled climber that inhabits tropical and subtropical wetlands and rainforests.

scaled snake often favours quite dense vegetation. Although primarily terrestrial, it often climbs to bask or forage in shrubs, epiphytic ferns and tree hollows. It hunts by both day and night, though the latter is favoured in hotter weather, preying mostly on mammals and frogs. From 5–18 young (average 10) are born per litter, but only every other year.

The rough-scaled snake is similar to the tiger snake in many ways. Its venom has similar effects on humans and although technically less toxic, it's nevertheless an extremely dangerous snake, capable of inflicting a life-threatening bite. Envenomation is characterised by bleeding, muscle damage, kidney failure and paralysis. The record for the longest period of complete paralysis following an Australian snakebite is more than three months – the culprit was a rough-scaled snake. It has a reputation for being extremely pugnacious and may bite repeatedly. In north-eastern NSW and adjacent Queensland this snake is common in some areas and is a major source of snakebites, which appear clinically similar to tiger snake bites and respond to tiger snake antivenom.

Broad-headed snakes

Dangerous species: *Hoplocephalus bungaroides* (broad-headed snake), *H. bitorquatus* (pale-headed snake), *H. stephensii* (Stephen's banded snake).

Distribution: These snakes are confined to eastern Australia. The broad-headed snake is found only in the Sydney geological basin in areas of Hawkesbury and Narrabeen sandstone outcrops. It favours the shelter of loose flat rocks, especially near the edges of cliffs or slopes. The pale-headed snake's habitat requirements are less specific. It occurs in a broad coastal strip from just north of Sydney through south-eastern Queensland to the south-eastern coast of Cape York. Stephen's banded snake extends from south-eastern Queensland into NSW, south almost as far as Sydney.

Pale-headed

Broad-headed

Stephen's banded

The broad-headed snake may reach 0.9 m in length and is distinctively coloured, with a black upper body and narrow, irregular cross-bands of yellow scales, which may link in a stripe laterally. The head has numerous yellow scales forming a dot pattern. The upper labial scales are barred with yellow, belly scales are grey to black. Specimens may be confused with young diamond pythons (*Morelia spilota spilota*) but differ in lacking heat-sensing pits on the lower lip and having enlarged scales on the top of the head.

The pale-headed snake may reach 0.8 m in length. It's generally light grey to brown above, with a distinctive pale-cream band on the nape of the neck, bordered posteriorly with a dark band. The head is grey, sometimes with black flecks, especially laterally. Belly scales are cream or light grey.

Stephen's banded snake may reach 1.3 m in length and is generally grey-brown above, with dark ragged-edged cross-bands. However, unbanded specimens have been recorded. The head is dark grey to black, with very pale patches on either side of the nape of the neck. The lips show pale barring.

The broad-headed snake is found in rocky sandstone areas, where it shelters under loose flat rocks. It may also utilise rock crevices and even tree hollows, especially during summer. It feeds principally on small lizards,

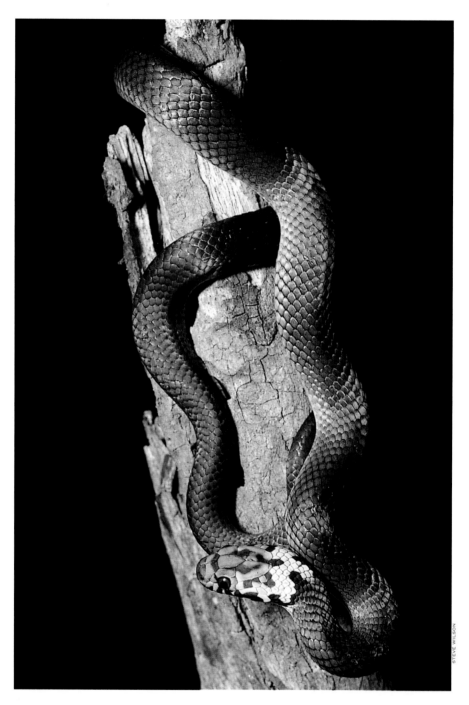

The pale-headed snake is a nocturnal tree-dwelling species that lives in hollow limbs and behind loose bark. It's most common near watercourses where it can catch its favourite food – tree frogs.

Climbing skills are rare among Australia's venomous snakes, but the broad-headed (above) and Stephen's banded snakes (below) can scale trees and rock faces with ease. They both display the same defensive posture, rearing their bodies in a tight S-shape, flattening their wide heads and flicking their tongues.

especially geckos and skinks. Because the rocks it favours are in demand for home landscaping, this snake's habitat is rapidly being destroyed, and it's now considered rare to endangered throughout its range. The female gives birth to about seven young in late summer every other year.

The pale-headed snake is primarily arboreal (tree-dwelling) and feeds on frogs, lizards and mammals. The female gives birth to about five young every other year.

Stephen's banded snake is both arboreal and terrestrial, exploiting rocky areas. It eats lizards, mammals – including bats – and birds. About six young are born every other year.

There is relatively little published on the venom and bites of any of the three species of broad-headed snake, but the author's experience with bites by *H. bungaroides* and *H. stephensii* clearly indicates that these snakes can cause severe bites, with a potentially lethal bleeding disorder. No fatalities have been reported, but a severe bite from a large specimen might prove fatal if inadequately treated. Tiger snake antivenom appears to be helpful in treatment.

Eastern small-eyed snake

Dangerous species: *Rhinoplocephalus nigrescens* (eastern small-eyed snake).
Distribution: Found from the coast to the ranges of eastern Australia, from Cape York to southern Victoria.

The eastern small-eyed snake is generally up to 0.5 m in length, though specimens up to 1.2 m have been recorded. It has a uniform, steely black body, with cream to pink belly scales, sometimes flecked with black. It may be mistaken for a juvenile red-bellied black snake, from which it differs in having very small eyes, and little or no red on the lower flanks.

Occupying a variety of habitats, the eastern small-eyed snake often shelters under loose flat rock or fallen timber and surface debris and is often

HAROLD COGGER

With its black back and pink belly, the eastern small-eyed snake is often mistaken for a young red-bellied black snake. This secretive species displays features common to many small, venomous nocturnal snakes; its eyes are greatly reduced in size, placing a strong reliance on other senses such as smell.

encountered under the bark of fallen trees. In winter, several snakes may shelter together; aggregations of up to 29 individuals having been recorded. Foraging at night, this snake relies on scent to detect its prey, chiefly reptiles and including smaller snakes. Females give birth to an average of four young in late summer; earlier in northern areas.

Few bites have been reported for this snake. The venom isn't especially toxic, but does cause muscle damage, and it's included here because progressive delayed muscle damage has caused at least one fatality. It doesn't appear to cause paralysis or bleeding, but kidney damage might occur in a severe case. Currently, tiger snake antivenom is suggested for severe cases, though there's little clinical experience to confirm its effectiveness.

Mulga snakes

Dangerous species: *Pseudechis australis* (mulga snake, king brown), *P. butleri* (Butler's mulga snake).
Distribution: The mulga snake occurs across most of mainland Australia with the exception of the southern and south-eastern coasts, Victoria and Tasmania. Butler's mulga snake is restricted to inland south-central WA.

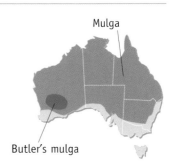

Mulga

Butler's mulga

The mulga snake is one of Australia's largest venomous snakes, sometimes exceeding 3 m in length. Its colour is generally a shade of brown, from almost black-brown through to pale or red-brown. Most body scales have a lighter, often yellow, inner edge, giving rise to a reticulated pattern. The belly is cream or yellow. The head is broad, not distinct from the neck, and the body is robust and generally thicker and more flattened than that of a brown snake (*Pseudonaja*) of the same length. Butler's mulga snake may reach 1.6 m in length. It's generally deep brown to black, with some scales having pale yellow or cream centres, giving a distinctive patterned appearance.

Mulga snakes may be found in a wide variety of habitats and will seek shelter in any available place, including animal burrows, under rocks, or under rubbish near houses. They are opportunistic feeders, eating lizards principally, but consuming everything from small mammals to reptile eggs. Butler's mulga snake feeds almost exclusively on lizards. Both species may be active by day or night, depending on the temperature and are egg layers, producing about nine eggs per clutch, usually laid in early to mid-summer, though gravid (pregnant) females have been found in autumn and even in winter.

The mulga snake is common over much of its range, while the status of Butler's mulga snake is less certain. Mulga snake bites are common in northern Australia, and in the NT they account for about half of all significant snakebites. Though its venom is less potent than that of brown and tiger snakes and taipans, the mulga snake can produce more venom than any other Australian species, injecting it through comparatively long fangs, making the proportion of severe bites high. Muscle damage, kidney failure and bleeding may all occur. A few deaths from mulga snake bite have been recorded but

STEVE WILSON

The mulga snake is also commonly called the king brown snake although it is actually a type of black snake. This species produces the highest venom yield of any Australian snake.

little is known about the venom and effects of bites by Butler's mulga snake, but it should be assumed that they are similar to those of the mulga snake. Mulga snake venom is used in the production of the confusingly named black snake antivenom, the most suitable treatment for major bites by both species of mulga snakes. Mulga snakes are technically brown-coloured members of the black snake genus. The antivenom's name arises from a tragic incident in the 1960s when a WA man who'd been bitten by a mulga snake died, despite treatment with brown and tiger snake antivenom. It was later discovered that the use of Papuan black snake antivenom was effective against mulga snake bites and, though it's no longer used, the name has persisted. The tragedy also led to the gradual abandonment of the mulga snake's other common name, king brown snake.

Red-bellied black snake

Dangerous species: *Pseudechis porphyriacus*
(red-bellied black snake, common black snake).
Distribution: Found in an arc from SA through
Victoria and NSW to south-eastern Queensland,
with isolated populations further north.

Although the red-bellied black snake may reach 1.8 m in length, most specimens are considerably smaller. It's distinctively coloured, always jet black above, with deep-red tinging of the lower lateral scales, usually grading to paler belly scales, which may also have deep-red tonings. This gives this handsome snake its distinctive appearance, truly a red-bellied, black-coloured snake – though in northern populations the red colouration is often less striking, more a faded pink than a true red.

The quintessential venomous snake of the urban and populated areas of eastern Australia, the red-bellied black snake was by far the most common cause of snakebite in the early years of European settlement. Although the species is still found in urban areas, it's been suggested that it's succumbing to habitat destruction and the introduction of the cane toad, which has poison glands on its shoulder. Feeding principally on frogs, red-bellied black snakes seem to have been particularly hard hit by the toad's arrival.

This snake is almost invariably found near water, either near watercourses or swamps or in rainforests. Its black body helps it to absorb the sun's heat, enabling it to maintain a high body temperature for long periods and it forages during the day and after dusk on warmer nights. The female gives birth to about 12 young, enclosed in membranous sacs from which they soon emerge, in late summer to early autumn. Red-bellied black snakes are the only members of their genus to produce live young.

The victim of an undeserved bad reputation, the red-bellied black is generally inoffensive and reluctant to bite. Its venom isn't especially potent and in humans causes neither paralysis nor bleeding. It sometimes causes muscle damage, but even then the effects are quite mild and not generally of medical concern. Thus the likelihood of a fatal bite from this snake is very

HAROLD COGGER

The red-bellied black snake is one of our most beautiful and familiar yet most misunderstood reptiles. Its distribution closely mirrors Australia's densely settled east and south-east, and bites are frequently recorded; however, there are no confirmed fatalities. In the northern parts of its range it has reportedly suffered declines caused by feeding on the poisonous introduced cane toad.

small. Indeed, there have been no confirmed deaths from red-bellied black snake bite, despite the very large number that have occurred, especially in the past. Nevertheless, bites often result in systemic envenomation, which although generally not life threatening, is often most unpleasant for the patient, who may experience severe abdominal pain, vomiting, diarrhoea, headache and feel generally miserable.

Antivenom therapy is usually not required but when it is, tiger snake antivenom is the first choice.

Collett's snake

Dangerous species: *Pseudechis colletti*
(Collett's snake).

Distribution: Restricted to arid parts
of inland central Queensland, especially
the deeply cracking blacksoil clays.

One of the most spectacularly coloured of all Australia's dangerous snakes, Collett's snake is rich brown to black above, with distinctive irregular cross-bands of pale-coloured scales, usually with a pink or salmon toning. The lateral scales often grade into a similar colour, with the belly scales cream or yellow-orange. Few could deny that this is a truly beautiful snake. Its length may exceed 2 m.

Feeding principally on small mammals, Collett's snake is most commonly encountered after rain. It shelters in deep cracks in the soil, in sinkholes and

The beautiful Collett's snake, strikingly blotched with pink or crimson, is a poorly known inhabitant of the cracking clay blacksoil plains of central Queensland. It avoids high daytime temperatures by hiding deep in the soil cracks.

under debris on the open, treeless blacksoil plains of central Queensland. Females lay an average of 12 eggs in late spring to early summer, usually preceding the summer monsoonal rains. The species is so poorly known that it wasn't until the 1970s that researchers discovered that it laid eggs rather than producing live young. When harassed, a Collett's snake will flatten its neck, inflate its body and hiss loudly.

Collett's snake venom is similar to that of the mulga snake in terms of its potency and effect on humans, thus severe muscle damage, bleeding and kidney damage may all occur in severe bites. There are no records of fatalities, but few bites have been reported and there is little doubt that this snake is potentially deadly. Either black snake or tiger snake antivenom may be used to treat serious cases.

Taipans

Dangerous species: *Oxyuranus scutellatus* (taipan), *O. microlepidotus* (inland taipan, fierce snake).

Distribution: The taipan is found in the northern Kimberley in WA, in isolated parts of the northern NT, and in a coastal band from Cape York to north-eastern NSW. The inland taipan is found on the blacksoil plains and related habitats from south-western Queensland into north-western NSW, and in north-eastern SA through the Eyre Basin as far west and south as Coober Pedy. Its known

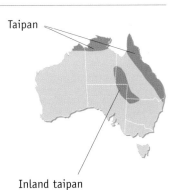

Taipan

Inland taipan

range is constantly being extended as more field work is undertaken in the unpopulated areas of arid inland Australia. Two specimens recorded from the Mildura region were probably washed down by floods in the north as it's unlikely that this species would be encountered in south-western NSW.

The taipan is Australia's largest venomous snake and individuals up to 4 m in length have been recorded. It's usually uniform brown above, varying from light to quite dark or russet, with a pale head, particularly on the snout. The head is long, with a prominent brow above the eye. Belly scales are pale yellow or cream, sometimes spotted with orange. The inland taipan is also a large snake, and has been known to exceed 2 m in length. It's generally deep olive to reddish-brown above, with dark speckling on the scales, sometimes creating a fine herringbone pattern. The head is often darker, sometimes glossy black, especially in winter. The inland taipan's colouration is similar to that of some colour forms of the western brown snake (*Pseudonaja nuchalis*), with which it may overlap in some regions. While both of these snakes are dangerous, the inland taipan's bite is more likely to be lethal and requires a different antivenom.

The taipan feeds exclusively on warm-blooded prey, especially rodents, and is often attracted to rubbish dumps, sugarcane fields and areas on farms where mice and rats abound. It's a swift, superbly adapted hunter with keen vision, foraging in the morning or late afternoon, and becoming nocturnal in hot weather. It will seek shelter in any available spot, including animal burrows, hollow logs and around dwellings. The inland taipan frequents the deep cracks in blacksoil plains where it feeds exclusively on mammals, especially the native plague rat, in whose burrows it may also shelter. Like the

The ecology of the inland taipan is inextricably linked to that of its main prey, the long-haired or plague rat. Together their fortunes rise and fall with the unpredictable rains that quench south-west Queensland's remote Channel Country.

STEVE WILSON

The taipan is one of the world's most lethal snakes. Its highly toxic venom and long fangs have evolved to swiftly immobilise prey, complementing its hunting strategy of bite, release, follow and eat.

taipan, it's most active in the early morning and may also be nocturnal during hot weather.

The taipan is an extremely dangerous snake. It's large, strikes swiftly, has the longest fangs of any Australian snake, and possesses abundant venom reserves. Although the inland taipan has the most toxic venom of any land snake in the world, that of the taipan is only slightly less so. It's also produced in greater quantity so is potentially even more deadly. Prior to the development of taipan antivenom, only two people are known to have survived a taipan bite. However, it isn't as aggressive as Australian folklore would have you believe and is infrequently encountered, attacking only when cornered. The inland taipan, despite being the world's most toxic land snake and having acquired the name fierce snake, is shy and disinclined to bite.

The venoms of both species are similar in their effects. They contain very powerful paralysing toxins and can cause severe bleeding, muscle damage and kidney failure. Taipan antivenom often needs to be administered in large quantities.

Spotted black snake

Dangerous species: *Pseudechis guttatus*
(spotted or blue-bellied black snake).
Distribution: Found in the interior of south-
eastern Queensland and eastern NSW north
from the Hunter Valley, where its range
extends to the coast.

The spotted black snake, also known as the blue-bellied black snake because of its dark underside, inhabits ranges and alluvial plains in the eastern interior from central NSW to southern Queensland.

STEVE WILSON

The spotted black snake grows to around 2 m in length. Its colour is variable, with some individuals a deep shiny black, like the red-bellied black snake, but with grey, deep-bluish or almost black belly scales. Others are a deeper grey-brown in colour, with a spotted appearance. The head is always dark.

The spotted black snake eats frogs, small mammals and lizards. Principally a daytime hunter, it will also forage after dusk on warm to hot nights. Females lay an average of 12 eggs in early summer.

Like Collett's snake, few spotted black snake bites have been recorded, although its similarity to the red-bellied black snake may have led to some spotted black snake bites being wrongly attributed to the latter. The venom is similar to the mulga snake's and until more information is available, it would be safest to assume that its bites are potentially more severe than those of the red-bellied black snake. Either tiger snake or black snake antivenom may be used to treat severe bites.

Death adders

Dangerous species: *Acanthophis antarcticus* (common death adder), *A. pyrrhus* (desert death adder), *A. praelongus* (northern death adder).
Distribution: Widespread throughout most of mainland Australia, excluding the south-eastern and south-western corners.

Common death adder

Northern death adder

Desert death adder

Death adders have a very distinctive body form, being more similar to true adders (family Viperidae) than to other elapid snakes and their behaviour mirrors this difference. They have wide, flattened, triangular heads, a narrow

STEVE WILSON

Death adders are sluggish snakes that use camouflage and immobility to hide from predators and prey. Lying concealed under leaf litter or overhanging foliage, this northern death adder would be virtually invisible to lizards, birds or an unwary bushwalker.

neck and a comparatively short, stout body tapering to a distinctive thin tail, which is used to lure prey. The scales, including those on the head, are keeled (ridged). The desert death adder is smaller (length to 75 cm) than the common death adder (1 m) and less robust in build, with more prominent keeling of scales and more rugose (rough) head shields. The northern death adder is somewhat intermediate between the two, and reaches 70 cm in length.

There are also subtle colour differences between the species. The common death adder is quite variable in body colour, from grey-brown to red-brown, usually with distinct, darker cross-bands. The belly is usually cream and the tail tip pale cream or even white. The head has darker brown edging on the lip scales forming a series of roughly parallel bars. The desert death adder is more reddish-brown in colour, often similar to the deep-red sand colour of parts of arid Australia, while the cross-bands may be bright yellow. The northern death adder is dark brown to grey-brown or reddish-brown, with narrow dark-edged cross-bands. The tail tip may be black or yellow.

Death adders are generally cryptic, relying on camouflage rather than escape when approached. This behaviour led to it being called the deaf adder in earlier times until, in the rush to avoid being labelled as "common" – at one time, the so-called lower-classes in Australia often pronounced "th" as "f", as London's Cockneys do today – the present name evolved.

Utilising a wide variety of habitats, from coastal dunes to hilly shrubland and even rocky areas, they shelter under leaf litter or low vegetation. Like the adders they so closely resemble, death adders are sit-and-wait or ambush predators, lying in wait for prey to pass. Their apparent indolence is, however, illusory, for if threatened they can strike rapidly and forcefully, using their comparatively long fangs and a large quantity of venom to inflict a potentially lethal bite. Because they're often found near animal-movement corridors, which may also often be used by humans, bites may occur when someone unwittingly steps close to one of these superbly camouflaged snakes. They are active both at night and during the day, depending on the region and the temperature. They eat a wide variety of prey, mostly small reptiles but also small mammals, birds and frogs; essentially any edible vertebrate within striking range. Between 10 and 34 live young are born in late summer.

In the past, death adders had a ferocious reputation, with half of all people bitten dying. In New Guinea they still exact a significant toll on human life, but in Australia the advent of antivenom, retrieval services and intensive-care medicine have meant that death adder bites are now only rarely fatal. This is in part because their venom, though potent and produced in large quantity, has only one major effect on humans: paralysis. But the type of paralysis caused is comparatively short-lived, reversible with antivenom therapy and associated neither with bleeding, muscle damage nor kidney failure, so with correct first aid and hospital treatment, deaths from death adder bite should continue to be very rare.

However, if someone in a very remote area was bitten – with medical aid unavailable and paralysis setting in before help could arrive – the outcome could be fatal. This emphasises the importance of prompt and correct first aid. Another reason for the rarity of fatalities due to death adder bites lies in the infrequency of attacks. In developed areas, death adder populations appear to have declined greatly in recent years, possibly due to the species' inability to adapt to habitat change.

SNAKE-SCALE TERMINOLOGY

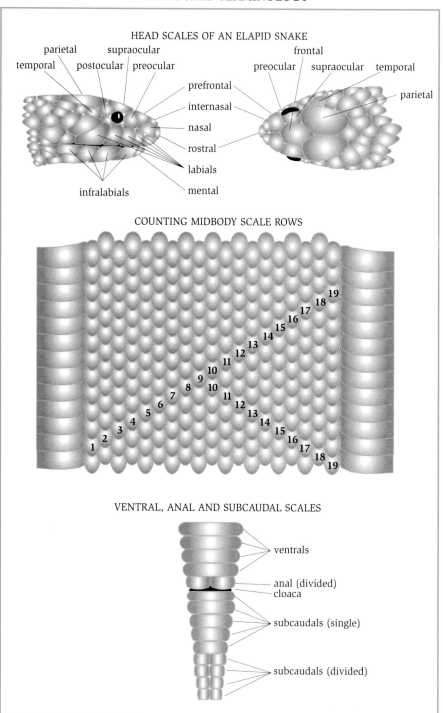

HEAD SCALES OF AN ELAPID SNAKE

parietal · supraocular · frontal
temporal · postocular · preocular · preocular · supraocular · temporal
parietal
prefrontal
internasal
nasal
rostral
labials
infralabials · mental

COUNTING MIDBODY SCALE ROWS

VENTRAL, ANAL AND SUBCAUDAL SCALES

ventrals

anal (divided)
cloaca

subcaudals (single)

subcaudals (divided)

SCALE CHARACTERISTICS OF DANGEROUS AUSTRALIAN SNAKES

Species	Body scales	Midbody* scales	Ventral scales	Anal scale	Subcaudal scales	Page
Eastern brown	smooth	17	185–235	divided	45–75, divided	24
Western brown	smooth	17/19	180–230	divided	50–70, divided	24
Peninsula brown	smooth	17	185–235	divided	45–75, divided	24
Spotted brown	smooth	19–21	190–220	divided	45–70, divided	24
Ingram's brown	smooth	17	190–220	divided	55–70, divided	24
Common tiger✧	smooth	15/17/19	140–190	single	35–65, undivided	28
Black tiger✧	smooth	15/17/19/21	155–190	single	40–60, undivided	28
Western tiger✧	smooth	15/17/19/21	155–190	single	40–60, undivided	28
Copperheads⚥	smooth	15	140–165	single	35–55, undivided	31
Rough-scaled	keeled	23	160–185	single	50–60, undivided	33
Broad-headed★	smooth	21	200–230	single	40–65, undivided	35
Pale-headed★	smooth	19/21	190–225	single	40–65, undivided	35
Stephen's banded★	smooth	21	220–250	single	50–70, undivided	35
Eastern small-eyed	smooth	15	165–210	single	30–45, undivided	38
Mulga	smooth	17	185–225	divided	50–75, divided posteriorly	40
Butler's mulga	smooth	17	200–220	divided	50–70, divided posteriorly	40
Red-bellied black	smooth	19	170–215	divided	45–65, divided posteriorly	42
Collett's	smooth	19	215–235	divided	50–70, divided posteriorly	44
Taipan	keeled	21–23	220–250	single	45–80, divided	45
Inland taipan	smooth	21–23	220–250	single	55–70, divided	45
Spotted black	smooth	19	175–205	divided	45–65, divided posteriorly	48
Common death adder✿	smooth /keeled	21	110–135	divided	35–60, mostly undivided	49
Desert death adder✿	keeled	19–21	120–160	divided	40–65, divided posteriorly	49
Northern death adder✿	keeled	23	110–135	divided	35–60, mostly undivided	49

*   Species for which numbers are separated by a slash exhibit only these scales counts.
    Numbers separated by a dash refer to a range.
✧   Large, squarish frontal scale
⚥   Enlarged lateral scales
★   Ventral scales keeled or notched
✿   Subocular scales present below the eye

Spiders prey mostly on insects, keeping in check all manner of garden and household pests. As is true of most spiders, the female Sydney funnel-web, pictured here, is larger than the male.

Chapter two

SPIDERS
AND INSECTS

P A U L   Z B O R O W S K I

Some of the creatures selected for inclusion in this book may, at first, seem surprising. Not everyone is aware of the care needed in handling living sea shells for example, but some have powerful poisons. For spiders, on the other hand, a general warning is unnecessary as most of us seem to have a built-in alarm that's triggered by their very presence.

Of the world's 30,000 or so known spider species, about 2000 are found in Australia, and many new species are described each year. Of these, less than 50 species are dangerous to people. A few more are suspected of being harmful, but as yet there is no definite evidence to prove them so. However, we do have the dubious honour of sharing the continent with the world's most dangerous spider species – the Sydney funnel-web spider. Part I of this chapter covers each of the spider species or groups whose bites are known to have hazardous effects on people.

All spiders produce toxins designed to subdue their prey, but few possess the right chemical mix in a high enough dose to be dangerous to humans, and many aren't large or powerful enough to penetrate the skin. The funnel-web spiders are the most dangerous exception on both counts, and the attention their toxicity has generated has resulted in the discovery of 38 different funnel-web species. A definite link to dangerous bites has only been established for four or five of these, but it's advisable to assume that all are dangerous.

These dire warnings, and our often horrified reactions to spiders and their relatives, help to keep us safe from the very few dangerous species, but there's another side to the world of eight-legged creatures. Spiders, as important predators, play a vital role in our environment and help to restrict populations of damaging agricultural pests. And when we look beyond their fearsome reputations and appearances, the world of spiders is a fascinating place, full of unexpected beauty and wonder.

In my travels, always looking at the small dwellers in my surroundings, I've been rewarded with numerous remarkable sights. I've seen webs teeming with hundreds of colourful baby spiders, watched large-eyed wolf spiders running down their prey on desert dunes and marvelled at the spectacular golden orb spiders sitting on webs spun of golden silk. I've sat in simple fascination as an orb spider constructed its complex web and been the audience for a jumping spider as it performed a dancing display on a leaf stage, spotlit by a forest sunbeam.

The tiny risk that a spider will do us harm is a small price to pay for the wonder they can instil in us if we make the effort to appreciate them. And of course, spare a thought for the millions of flies and other irritating insects that spiders do away with every single day.

Part II of this chapter covers some of the potentially dangerous insects found in Australia. Many insects are toxic themselves, making them unpalatable to predators, but the use of actual venoms is less common. Their real threat to humans comes from allergic reactions to the defensive bites and spines of some, and the spread of disease by others. Bees, for example, cause about the same number of fatalities each year as crocodiles, sharks or snakes, through allergic reactions to their stings. Similarly, the seemingly harmless mosquito can carry diseases such as malaria, dengue fever and encephalitis, all of which can be fatal. But as with the other animals featured in this book, the actual risks associated with these creatures are small, and with a little knowledge, the threats they pose are easily defused.

SPIDERS

Spiders are an ancient group, appearing in the fossil record around 400 mya and predating the age of modern insects. They belong to the invertebrate class Arachnida, which contains 11 groups of eight-legged creatures, nine of which are found in Australia. Other well-known arachnids include scorpions, ticks and mites.

A spider's body is composed of an abdomen, or hind body, and a head region, called a cephalothorax. The cephalothorax bears the hollow, venom-injecting fangs (or chelicerae), other mouthparts, and legs. The top of the cephalothorax is known as the carapace and it's here that the eyes are situated. Most spiders have eight eyes, although some have lost one or two pairs during their evolution and few have sufficiently good vision to use it as their main sense when seeking prey, most "feeling" or "sensing" their surroundings with trichobothria, sensory hairs that detect vibrations and air movement. All spiders are hunters, and are important predators in most habitats, eating mainly insects.

Silk production is another trait shared by all spiders, although the burrow-dwelling species tend to use silk for lining their refuges rather than for constructing prey-catching webs. In either case, a great deal of information about prey, mates and predators is transmitted by vibrations along the webs. Silk is also put to amazing use for dispersal. Excellent colonisers of new habitats, spiders are found everywhere outside of the extremes of the open oceans and polar regions. Young spiders of some species release long strands of silk that are caught by the wind, carrying them off and on occasions spiders have been observed drifting along at up to 5000 m altitude. This spectacular means of dispersal is called ballooning, and using this technique spiders can cross a suburban backyard or travel vast distances in search of new habitats to colonise.

In general, the above-ground, web-building spiders encountered in the open are not dangerous. Of greatest risk to humans are some ground-dwelling spiders, the most important of which are introduced in this section. In some of these cases it isn't only the venom that is of concern. Anecdotal reports

ESTHER BEATON

During summer, male funnel-web spiders leave their burrows in search of a female to mate with, often coming into contact with people in the process.

suggest that some spider species have flesh-eating bacteria on their fangs and/or in their gut. Apparently these are sometimes introduced into bite wounds, leading to potentially serious complications. As similar bacteria live freely in the soil, the link between spider bites and these so-called "necrotic" reactions, is still an unresolved and controversial issue (see the white-tailed spider entry on page 65 for more information on necrosis).

As is the case for snakebite treatment, it's important to know which species is responsible for a bite to ensure that the correct antivenom is administered. It's rare, however, for victims to have the presence of mind and necessary skill to catch the culprit without exposing themselves to further risk. Some prior knowledge of the general appearance of dangerous species is therefore desirable.

Two other groups of arachnids – ticks and scorpions – are also covered here. The paralysis tick is dangerous to domestic pets, and can be so to children. The Australian species of scorpion are not particularly dangerous to humans, but retain an undeserved reputation acquired by association with their more venomous overseas relatives.

Centipedes belong to another group of invertebrates, the class Chilopoda, and feature here for the memorable pain of their bites. Because most centipedes live in the soil, their bites may expose the victim to soil-dwelling bacteria, including tetanus. It's therefore advisable to disinfect such bites and be sure to be up-to-date with tetanus shots. Similar advice holds for bites from large ground-dwelling spiders or any other gardening injury that breaks the skin.

Sydney funnel-web spider

Family: Hexathelidae; subfamily: Atracinae.
Dangerous species: *Atrax robustus*.
Distribution: NSW; an area around Sydney extending from the Hunter River in the north, to Nowra in the south, and west to Lithgow.

Funnel-web spiders belong to the suborder Mygalomorphae, a group of stout, primitive and mainly ground-dwelling species. Unlike spiders of the suborder Araneomorphae – the modern open-range hunters and web weavers – their large fangs work up and down, rather than sideways. The female Sydney funnel-web's body is about 35 mm long, while the more dangerous male grows to about 25 mm. The species is black all over, its colour distinguishing it from the similar mouse and trapdoor spiders that usually have other hues mixed with black or brown. The members of this genus are distinguished by serrations on the inside of the fangs and an elongated last segment of the longer spinnerets. These features are difficult to see in the field and so, because many mygalomorph spiders are dangerous, it's safer to assume the worst when faced with something that looks like a funnel-web.

The Sydney funnel-web is recognised as the world's deadliest spider. The most dangerous component of its venom is a neurotoxin or nerve poison called delta-atracotoxin, which is present in much higher doses in males. The Sydney funnel-web has two related species (genus *Atrax*) extending to south-eastern NSW and into the Snowy Mountains. The toxicity of these species is unknown but is presumed to be very dangerous.

Funnel-web spiders are nocturnal and spend the day in silk-lined burrows. They require a humid environment so the entrances to their burrows are

When threatened, a Sydney funnel-web spider raises its body and front legs in the direction of its harasser, exposing its impressive fangs.

ESTHER BEATON

hidden under logs, stones, tussocks or around houses. They're most often encountered at night during the warmer months, when the males wander in search of females. Digging in the moister parts of the garden may uncover funnel-webs during the day, and when disturbed they can be very aggressive. Anyone who has seen one in attack posture, front legs raised and long fangs held high and ready to strike, will not only make sure always to use gardening gloves, but will probably go out and buy an even stouter pair.

The immediate effect of a bite is severe pain at the site, followed by sweating, muscle tremors and a spreading of the pain and cramps to other parts of the body. If the bite is from a male, the victim will require the administration of antivenom as quickly as possible, otherwise the result will be uncontrollable muscle contractions followed by coma and possibly death. At least 13 people are known to have died from funnel-web bites between 1927 and 1980, when the antivenom became widely available. It took nearly 30 years to produce the final working version of the antivenom, development being hampered by the lack of suitable test animals (delta-atracotoxin is only toxic to humans and mice under the age of a few days). All that hard work has paid off – there's only been one death attributed to Sydney funnel-web envenomation (the result of a misdiagnosis) since 1980.

The other funnel-web spiders

Family: Hexathelidae; subfamily: Atracinae.

Dangerous species: *Hadronyche versutus* (Blue Mountains funnel-web), *H. formidabilis* (northern tree funnel-web), and probably all 38 species in this subfamily.

Distribution: Restricted to the more temperate and humid areas of the east coast and ranges, from Tasmania to southern Queensland. Pockets of remnant humid forest are their link to a once-wetter continent. One species is separated from this pattern in the Eyre Peninsula of SA, and another in the Mossman area of northern Queensland.

ESTHER BEATON

The exact toxicity of the Blue Mountains funnel-web's venom isn't known, but it's safest to assume that it's potentially deadly and give the spider a wide berth.

As an entomologist, I'm frequently presented with spiders by people who want to know if they've found a funnel-web. They often seem disappointed when I assure them that none of these fabled beasts live in their particular region. However, our knowledge of the funnel-webs' range is far from perfect, and it's sure to continue expanding as new species are discovered and new areas explored.

The very fine features that distinguish funnel-web species from each other are not useful in the field. The Blue Mountains variety is slightly smaller than its Sydney cousin; the female's body length is 32 mm and the male's 18 mm. The female northern tree funnel-web reaches a formidable 50 mm in length when fully grown (the species bears the very appropriate Latin name of *H. formidabilis*), the more slender male growing to 35 mm.

Only some of the 35 species of *Hadronyche* have common names. They are found in wet forests from the Hunter Valley, NSW, north to the south-eastern highlands of Queensland. Their shallow, web-covered retreats are usually under the bark of rainforest trees, both fallen and standing and the spider may be found up to 30 m above ground. Unlike the Sydney funnel-web, it seems that it's the females of the other funnel-web species that are the most dangerous.

Other tree-dwelling funnel-webs are distributed over the wet forests of the east. The Blue Mountains funnel-web shares its coastal range with the Sydney funnel-web, but also extends out to the drier hills as far west as Orange, a rarity for this humidity-loving group. Its burrows tend to have a web-lined entrance hidden under a log.

All of the species in this genus should be regarded as very dangerous. The few recorded bites from the northern tree funnel-web have resulted in serious and painful symptoms leading to a semi-comatose state. Administration of the antivenom for the Sydney funnel-web has resulted in full cures, but in some cases a dose four times greater than usual was required. The Blue Mountains funnel-web produces the same amount of venom as the Sydney funnel-web, but there haven't been any recorded bites, probably due to its very retiring habits.

Red-back spider

Family: Theridiidae.
Dangerous species: *Latrodectus hasselti*
(previously known as *L. mactans*).
Distribution: Australia-wide.

The red-back spider is found in drier habitats, from sclerophyll forests to deserts. Similar species, known as black widows, occur all over the world. The larger females are shiny, smooth, black spiders with an hourglass-shaped red marking on the underside, and a red to orange stripe on top. The female is around 10 mm in length and has long, thin, black legs. Males are less than 5 mm long, tend to be lighter and are too small to bite people.

Red-backs find human dwellings very attractive and have developed a fabled association with us. Their typically messy, dense, white webs are a familiar sight in the corners and overhangs of Australian houses. The webs are usually at least as deep as they are wide, and the female spider hides out of view during the day. Somewhere below the web is a series of ingenious vertical, sticky threads that are held taut by a complex series of "guide-rope" threads. When an insect walking past gets entangled, the vertical lines snap and propel the prey up off the ground, where the spider can subdue it.

These spiders rarely leave their webs and aren't aggressive, but due to their urban proliferation, several thousand people are bitten in Australia each year. The initial bite apparently doesn't hurt, but pain and a burning sensation develop about five minutes later. Reactions vary, but sweating, stiffness, muscle weakness and tremors are common. The symptom most specific to a red-back bite is localised sweating around the bite area. Before an antivenom was developed in 1956, 13 people were known to have died from red-back bites. No deaths have been recorded since.

The brilliant stripe of the female red-back spider is unmistakable. Despite their deadly reputation, red-backs are neither fast nor aggressive and bites usually only occur when they are accidentally picked up.

White-tailed spider

Family: Gnaphosidae.
Dangerous species: *Lampona cylindrata.*
Distribution: Found throughout Australia
and New Zealand.

The white-tailed spider has reddish legs and an elongated, cylindrical body, around 20 mm in length. The dark body always has a whitish tip to the abdomen, and sometimes two or four light spots on the sides.

These spiders are roaming nocturnal hunters, building a small sac-like web to hide in, rather than for prey capture. They feed primarily on other spiders, which they often lure ingeniously by imitating the vibrations of insects caught

As white-tailed spiders age they become darker, changing from dark plum to almost black with each successive moult, but the distinctive white spot on the end of the abdomen always remains.

in their webs. Outside, they live under bark and logs, but they do move into houses, especially in summer, and are often seen wandering on the floor and walls at night.

The white-tailed spider's bite isn't remarkable for its pain, but can cause variable symptoms, including a burning sensation, headache, nausea and chills. Because these spiders are common, they are blamed for many indoor bites, even in cases where the specimen isn't seen or caught to prove the link. White-tails have also attracted attention because of a presumed but unproven association between their bite and necrotic effects.

Because spiders are restricted to a liquid diet, they inject a flesh-dissolving enzyme during or after an initial bite. In humans, this usually results in only minor blistering and some local cell death. However, bacteria present in the gut and on the fangs of white-tails and many other spider species, may cause more serious blistering and ulceration of the skin.

At present there's some controversy about the nature of the necrotic effects from white-tail bites, and indeed from spider bites in general. It's possible that the bacteria enter the wound after the event, as they are freely present in the environment, especially in soil. Assuming that an indoor spider is responsible for the necrosis, a species emerging as a prime suspect is the black house spider (page 68). Until the debate is resolved white-tailed spiders should be considered dangerous.

There are few treatments available that provide a reliable cure for the necrosis. The primary treatment involves scraping flesh from the bite site and then slowly rehabilitating it with skin grafts. Recently, a cream based on the amino acid L-cystine has worked as a cure in some cases, and aloe vera rubbed liberally on the area seems to be of assistance.

Mouse spiders

Family: Actinopodidae.

Dangerous species: *Missulena bradleyi* (large mouse spider), *M. occatoria* and *M. insigne* (red-headed mouse spiders).

Distribution: Found in most parts of Australia, though more common in the humid regions.

Male and female mouse spiders look so different that on several occasions they have been described as different species. Females such as this one are typically black-brown in colour while some males have a bright-red carapace and gunmetal-blue abdomen.

The family containing the mouse spiders is part of the suborder Mygalomorphae, which also includes the funnel-webs. They are stout spiders with very broad heads, large downward-acting fangs and relatively short legs. Body length varies from 15 to 25 mm. The most obvious difference between mouse and funnel-web spiders is the head, which in the former is broader, raised at the front and has the eight eyes spread across the entire width. Funnel-webs and other mygalomorphs have the eyes grouped centrally. Mouse spiders may be brown, grey or black, and the male red-headed mouse spider has a spectacular combination of a bright red head and a blue abdomen.

Mouse spiders belong to a wider group known as trapdoor spiders, many of which live in burrows with a well-disguised, hinged lid. The name mouse spider comes from the female's habit of digging burrows more than 1 m deep. Females spend most of their lives in or near these burrows but males rarely dig in; they wander around looking for females, especially after rain. Unlike funnel-webs, mouse spiders tend to roam during the day.

Little is known of this group's venom, but a study of female red-headed mouse spiders indicated that their venom killed baby mice quicker than a funnel-web's. Fortunately, the burrow-bound females are rarely encountered and only a single confirmed bite from a male large mouse spider has been recorded. The victim – a 19-month-old southern Queensland girl – was bitten and went into a coma 15 minutes later. She was saved by funnel-web antivenom and recovered fully. Mouse spiders are not as aggressive as funnel-webs and so bites are rare, but as their toxins are potentially very dangerous, they should be treated with caution.

Black house spiders

Family: Desidae.
Dangerous species: *Badumna insignis* (large black house spider), *B. longinqua* (small black house spider).
Distribution: The large black house spider is found Australia-wide and, because it prefers dry climates, it's the species most likely to be found in the west. The small black house spider is found mainly in the moister east, south to Tasmania and in New Zealand.

Identification is aided by the house spider's other common name of window spider, which stems from its habit of building its web against a backing like a window frame, preferably in a corner. The lacy, messy web conceals a stout, almost black, velvet-textured spider, about 15 mm in length. On close inspection the abdomen has a fine, mottled pattern composed of lighter hairs.

Corner webs have a funnel-shaped retreat in which the spider hides during the day. Apart from windows, they adorn any secluded position: under eaves, gutters, in brickwork and among rocks and bark. In bushland the black house

DENSEY CLYNE

The messy white webs of the black house spider are a common sight in the nooks and crannies around a house. The spider waits patiently in its web tunnel for hapless insects to become entangled.

spider often builds its web in a tree that has been attacked by wood-boring insects. The insect damage causes the tree to produce sap, which attracts many insects, food for the waiting spider. Black house spiders are themselves often prey for the white-tailed spider.

Black house spiders are very shy and so their bites are uncommon, though memorable. The larger species from the west has more venom and has been responsible for more recorded bites. Symptoms include severe pain, nausea, vomiting, perspiration, headaches and giddiness. There is no antivenom as these effects are generally not long lasting and recovery is complete.

Paralysis ticks

Order: Acarina.

Dangerous species: *Ixodes holocyclus, I. cornuatus.*

Common names: Paralysis tick, dog tick, scrub tick.

Distribution: The Australian paralysis tick is confined to moister areas of the east coast and ranges from about Cooktown, Queensland, to the Gippsland region in Victoria. The lesser-known species, *I. cornuatus*, has also been implicated in paralysis; it's found in moist highlands from NSW to Tasmania.

A tick larva is about 1 mm long and better known for its itch and the allergic reactions it sometimes causes than for its appearance. The more venomous adult females are about 3 mm long before feeding, and swell to 15 mm when fully engorged. Their colour varies from light cream to dark grey, usually with some blue hues.

Paralysis ticks are familiar to many people as "dog" ticks. Thousands of dogs and other domestic animals die each year from their venom, while others are cured with an expensive serum. Ticks are native species that feed on native mammals, particularly bandicoots, which become immune to their toxins due to constant exposure.

There are three free-living stages in the tick life cycle and they bite at each stage. Huge numbers of eggs scattered over grass and other vegetation hatch into six-legged larvae that attach to a host, feed on blood for a few days and then drop off. These moult into eight-legged nymphs that attach again for about a week. After dropping off they moult into adults. The adult males don't feed but move onto a host in search of a female with which to mate. When an adult female climbs onto a host it seeks a moist, dark place to attach; favourite sites on humans include the scalp, armpits and groin. Unless removed they will feed there for a week or more, swelling by up to 100 times their original size.

Ticks have only rudimentary sense organs and when it comes time to attach to a host they simply climb onto some vegetation and wait for something to brush past. The moment this happens they cling on with their pincers and crawl to a sheltered site to attach and start feeding.

PAUL ZBOROWSKI

When fully engorged, these adult female paralysis ticks will drop off the host and produce as many as 2000 eggs before they wither and die. As illustrated here, paralysis ticks come in a variety of colours.

Many people have a mild allergic reaction to the adult female's bite, and would quickly notice the itching and swelling and find and remove the tick. However, reactions in some people can be extremely severe and have been fatal. If the swelling is around the neck, it can lead to serious breathing difficulties. Antihistamine drugs and asthma inhalers can help in these cases. People may also become sensitised to the toxin after multiple bites.

Ticks don't actually possess a venom but produce the toxin only after they've been attached for 3–5 days. Hence the paralysis toxin isn't generally dangerous to adults because they will find and remove the tick before it has begun to produce it. Children, on the other hand, are at risk because they are less likely to notice the tick. Early symptoms such as weakness, fretfulness and diarrhoea are easily confused with other afflictions, but checking for ticks when such symptoms appear is advised, especially if the child has recently spent time in the bush. Actual paralysis can start from the limb extremities in about five days, coinciding with the production of the toxin.

The best method for removing a tick is quite contentious. It's important not to squeeze the body as more toxins may be injected and cause far worse reactions. Daubing the tick with alcohol, insect repellent or pyrethrum-based spray will cause it to die and sometimes fall off. Very fine tweezers can be used with great care to grab only the barbed feeding tube and pull the tick out. If the tick is engorged it's advisable to have it removed by a medical practitioner who will have the facilities available to deal with any reactions that may occur if the tick releases toxins during removal.

Removing the tick is essential and medical observation important. An antitoxin has been developed for dogs and works very well on them, but people may experience unpleasant side effects and it should only be used as a last resort. Most human patients recover over time without the antitoxin. The gene associated with the toxin's production was recently isolated and a vaccine is currently being developed.

Prevention is the best strategy. After spending time in grassland and bush in tick-prone areas, always check yourself, children and pets. Most insect repellents work on ticks and their use is advisable, especially if you're prone to allergic reactions.

Scorpions and centipedes

Scorpions
Order: Scorpiones.

Centipedes
Class: Chilopoda.

Dangerous species: No Australian species are considered dangerous, but stings can cause severe pain.

Distribution: Found all over Australia, with more and larger species in the warmer north.

Scorpions have a unique combination of an eight-legged body with large pincers at the front and a barbed tail. They're so distinctive that it's unlikely they'd be confused with anything else. Centipedes, however, are sometimes confused with millipedes. The former may be recognised by their flattened body, single pair of legs on each body segment and large sideways-acting

RICHARD THWAITES

Scorpions hold prey in place with their pincers and then arch the long sting over their backs to envenomate it. The effect on humans of the Australian scorpions' venom is poorly known.

fangs. Millipedes are generally cylindrical, have two pairs of legs on each body segment and lack visible fangs.

In other parts of the world, especially the tropical regions of America and Africa, scorpions are responsible for many deaths. The venom of the Australian species and its effects on humans are very poorly known; two deaths have been attributed to scorpions but they aren't well documented. Because the northern species grow larger, their stings can inject more venom but size is no indicator of scorpion danger. The dangerous scorpions around the world are all members of the family Buthidae. In Australia these are among the smallest of scorpions but in both of the scorpion-related fatalities, a small buthid was implicated. Local pain and swelling that may last a few days are the most common symptoms and nausea has been reported in a few cases. The poison isn't well understood and no antivenom has been developed as it isn't considered to be sufficiently dangerous.

Centipedes are fast, scurrying creatures, famous for their bite, but not responsible for any deaths in Australia. Once, lying in my swag in the Australian desert, I experienced the reaction of a cornered 12 cm individual, and can personally attest that their bites produce sudden, very memorable pain. The larger the individual the more venom may enter the wound, and individuals up to 18 cm long have been recorded.

Both scorpions and centipedes are nocturnal, hiding in burrows and under stones, logs and bark during the day. The adage "something nasty in the woodpile" applies to them both. Scorpions tend to be shy and sting only when accidentally cornered or stepped on. Centipedes on the other hand generally react aggressively to disturbance. Many people have learnt that a good way to get bitten is to attack them with a stick. It's worth noting that the possession of numerous claw-tipped legs makes the normally ground-dwelling centipede a quick climber. As with all biting and stinging creatures, leaving them alone is the best policy.

The large, sideways-acting jaws of centipedes are capable of inflicting a painful but usually not dangerous bite. Centipedes prefer dark places and will scurry away in search of cover if exposed during the day.

INSECTS

Considering the fact that insect species number in the millions, it's remarkable that so few are directly dangerous to humans. If the number of species is anything to go by, they're the most successful group of organisms on the planet, occupying almost every available habitat. We tend, however, to notice only the less than 1 per cent of species that damage our crops or are a nuisance in our homes. Among the rest are many species that greatly benefit humans by controlling other insect pests and pollinating crops, and performing essential ecological roles such as breaking down dead vegetable and animal matter and providing food for other animals.

A typical insect's body is composed of a head, thorax and abdomen and is protected by a tough, water-resistant external skeleton. This exoskeleton enables insects to transfer more power along their limbs than can a similarly sized "soft" creature, resulting in the legendary strength of insects such as ants. Another factor in their success is the evolution of wings around 300 mya, which gave them a new means of escaping predators and allowed them to fill previously empty ecological niches.

The order Hymenoptera contains the wasps, bees and ants. The sterile workers of many hymenopteran species have venomous stings that they use to defend their nests and can cause severe reactions in people sensitive to them. Another form of defence used by some insects is irritation. Some caterpillars (order Lepidoptera) have hairs and barbs that can deliver burning, itching and other painful reactions. To most people these bites, stings and irritations cause only temporary pain, but for others, repeated bites can mean serious or even life-threatening allergic reactions (page 165). But the most serious threat from the insect world lurks elsewhere.

It's been estimated that up to half of all the humans who have ever lived died as a result of diseases and parasites transmitted by the humble mosquito, yet of the thousands of species worldwide, with 300 or so in Australia, only a few have been implicated in disease transmission. Mosquitoes represent an important link in many food chains; fish feed on their larvae, while adult mosquitoes are consumed by everything from other insects to birds and bats. However, the few disease-carrying species that specialise in biting humans pose a serious risk.

Bull ants

Family: Formicidae; subfamily: Myrmeciinae.
Dangerous species: Many species of the genus *Myrmecia*.
Common names: Bulldog ant, jumper ant, jack-jumper, sergeant ant.
Distribution: The genus is found Australia-wide, with more species in the east than the interior. The jack-jumper is a small south-eastern species, the name jumper ant refers to at least two large species in NSW and Queensland, and in WA at least one species is known as sergeant ant.

Bull ants are most easily identified by their large size. The body of a foraging worker is 2–3 cm long, has a pronounced, elongated waist and very large, toothed mandibles or jaws that can be twice as long as the head.

The names that these creatures have inspired reflect their behaviour rather well. The workers are often pugnacious and will attack any intruder approaching their large nests. Jumping species have a very skittish walk and can jump suddenly, up to a height of 5 cm. As an insatiably curious naturalist, I've closely watched the brief and startling process of being bitten. The large, strong jaws, although fearsome, are not the problem: the ant only uses them to latch onto its victim while it curves its abdomen forward and jabs with its short, needle-like sting.

Bull ants are usually encountered in the bush rather than close to home, and the danger zone is around the nest. They are especially active on warm days and will stream out of the nest when workers on the surface are provoked. Their nests consist of deep, underground galleries, sometimes topped with a conspicuous volcano-like mound of excavated dirt. It's interesting to note that despite their huge jaws, adult bull ants, like all ants,

PAUL ZBOROWSKI

Although the large serrated jaws of this 20 mm bull ant look fearsome, it's the sting at the other end of the creature that inflicts pain. The jaws are used to hang on while the sting on the abdomen is inserted.

eat only liquid food. The hapless insects carried into the bowels of a nest are food for the white, grub-like larvae, which devour at least some of their food as solids.

Ants can be likened to wasps, from which they evolved, so it's not surprising that many sting as a method of defence. Unlike bee stings, which have backward-pointing barbs, ant stings are smooth and fully retract after use. It's the venom injected via the sting that causes the sudden sharp pain. Bull ant venom is, in itself, not a dangerous poison and usually causes only local pain. However, like many wasp venoms it can result in allergic reactions, especially after repeated stings, which can be serious and even life threatening.

Bees and wasps

Bees

Family: Apidae.

Wasps

Family: Vespidae.

Dangerous species: Serious allergic reactions can result from the stings of honeybees, *Apis mellifera*; the native paper wasps of the genera *Polistes* and *Ropalidia*; and the introduced European wasps *Vespula germanica* and *V. vulgaris*.

Distribution: Bees and paper wasps are found all over Australia, while the introduced European wasp is, at present, restricted to the temperate south from Tasmania to northern NSW and west to southern WA.

Bees and wasps

European wasp

The females of many wasp species have a needle-like, egg-laying organ called an ovipositor. The ovipositors of sterile workers of the social wasps and ants are modified into a sting that's used for injecting venom into prey and defending nests. The bee has a barbed sting that latches on so securely that when the bee flies away it rips free, leaving the venom sac and barb embedded; the bee subsequently dies. It's important not to remove a honey-bee barb by squeezing it with the fingers, as this will pump in more venom. Unless you have very fine tweezers with which to grasp the barb only, use a scratching sideways motion to dislodge it. Apply an ice pack and seek medical help if prone to strong allergic reactions.

The paper wasps have small, sharp, barbless stings that can be reused. They aren't aggressive when foraging, but if you blunder near or bump into a nest, a horde may emerge and inflict many stings. Most nests are found in the bush, suspended under leaves or in tree canopies. Closer to home, some species suspend nests from wire fences and others build under the eaves of houses.

Nests of European wasps are buried underground or in house walls. In Europe, they have a short life cycle that's completed during the warm part of the year. The queens then overwinter and renew the cycle the following season. In Australia's warmer climate, colonies can survive year-round, so

Honeybees fuel their foraging flights with nectar from the flowers they visit, recognising and rejecting blooms that have just been visited by another honeybee.

Paper wasp nests are often built under the eaves of houses. Each sealed chamber contains a paralysed caterpillar, which will serve as food for the wasp larva developing alongside it.

their nests can grow to several metres across and contain more than 100,000 individuals. If you have to get rid of wasps that are nesting too close for comfort, place a plastic bag around the nest at night when they are inactive and then use a knock-down spray, sealing the bag when the nest has been cut down. Many wasps benefit humans by feeding on caterpillars that may damage gardens, so destroying a colony should be a last resort. However, European wasps may pose a serious threat to children and domestic pets and can also invade and destroy the hives of domestic honeybees.

If you're prone to allergic reactions, repeated bites from any wasp or bee can be very serious. An immunotherapy treatment that slowly brings the immune system's over-reaction back to safer levels is available.

Stinging caterpillars

Families: Thaumetopoeidae (processionary
caterpillars), Limacodidae (cup moths),
Lymantriidae (tussock moths), Anthelidae,
Notodontidae, Arctiidae (tiger moths) and
Eupterotidae.
Common names: Hairy caterpillars, cup moths,
Chinese junks, slug caterpillars, processionary
caterpillars, bag shelter moths.
Distribution: As so many species are involved, it's
unlikely that any part of Australia lacks some type
of irritating or stinging caterpillar.

Stinging caterpillars use two main defensive strategies: poisonous hairs and
venomous spines. Both lead to skin irritations, weals, pain and sometimes
serious allergic reactions.

**Many cup moth caterpillars have venom glands attached to their spines.
The spines have weakened tips that rupture under pressure, releasing venom
from the gland.**

PAUL ZBOROWSKI

The more common strategy is that of the hairy caterpillars. In some species each hair's base is attached to a poison gland. If you pick up or brush against one of these caterpillars the hairs are shed and become embedded in your skin. Some species have so-called "dart hairs" that can detach in their thousands. Sometimes wind alone may cause this to happen, explaining some of the baffling cases of skin irritations experienced after time spent in the bush.

The most remarkable of these caterpillars are the processionary caterpillars of the bag shelter moths. They dwell in large silk bags full of droppings and detritus that hang in wattle trees. When it's time to feed, the caterpillars crawl out of the bag and go walkabout in a perfect nose-to-tail procession. This often happens at night and the train simply heads up to the tree canopy.

When these processionary caterpillars have stripped their food tree they will go in search of another in a head-to-tail line, following a trail of silk laid down by the leader and added to by successive caterpillars.

PAUL ZBOROWSKI

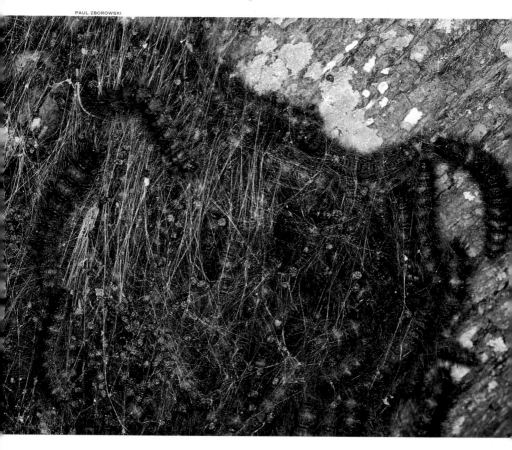

PAUL ZBOROWSKI

When this cup moth caterpillar is attacked it extends hidden spines from four protruberances at either end, delivering a venom that causes a stinging sensation not unlike that of a nettle.

When a tree has been stripped bare, however, tangled trains of caterpillars from a complete nest, up to tens of metres long, can be seen wandering in search of a new home. Stay away, as the surrounding area is full of their hairs. Not all hairy species use venom, but enough do to make avoidance the best policy for all of them.

The other defensive strategy employs non-detaching, venom-producing spines. Cup moth caterpillars are famous for these and for their extraordinary appearance, prompting names like slug caterpillar and Chinese junk. They are brightly coloured in greens, yellows and reds, and their skin is smooth and snail-like. On top are several projections resembling sea anemones. The common species are 2–3 cm long and live on eucalypt leaves in most areas.

Poison hairs initially cause a stinging and itching sensation, followed by a localised weal and maybe a rash. Because histamine is a component of many of these poisons, a strong allergic reaction may follow. A jab from a cup moth caterpillar spine will produce pain and a weal.

The hairs need to be removed gently, one by one if possible, or using a band-aid or sticky tape. The use of calamine lotion should be enough to ease the temporary symptoms. If more serious allergic reactions occur, or if caterpillar hairs get into your eyes, seek medical attention.

Mosquitoes and disease

Family: Culicidae.

Dangerous species: *Aedes aegypti* (dengue mosquito), *Aedes* spp. (several can carry Ross River fever), *Culex* spp. (can carry Ross River fever, encephalitis), *Anopheles* spp. (some can carry malaria).

Distribution: The mosquito genera mentioned above are distributed all over Australia, but the various diseases they sometimes carry are restricted to particular regions, as discussed below. These distributions vary over time according to prevailing climatic conditions.

Culex annulirostris

Anopheles farauii   *Aedes aegypti*

Most mosquitoes are about 5 mm long, too small to identify without a hand lens. However, as a general rule, each of the three disease-carrying genera has a characteristic sitting position. *Aedes* tend to sit parallel to the surface, low on their legs and with the hind legs raised. *Culex* also sit horizontally, but have all legs on the surface and sit high. *Anopheles* are famous for their 45-degree sitting posture, with their rear end and back legs high off the surface, pointing upwards.

A mosquito's bite isn't venomous – it's usually just annoying. It can, however, introduce viral and/or parasitic diseases that, between them, have been the biggest killers in human history. Some of these diseases are endemic to Australia while others only occur here when brought in from overseas. Four of the major diseases are discussed below.

Dengue or breakbone fever

This virus occurs in four distinct strains and is found throughout the tropics. It's occasionally introduced to Queensland, the only State where the main mosquito carrier is found. After an epidemic in the 1950s it was forgotten;

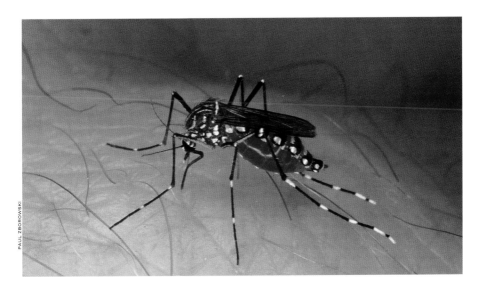

The abdomen of a mosquito like this *Aedes aegypti* can expand to twice its normal size to accommodate a large meal of blood. Only the female bites, using the blood to nourish her developing eggs.

however, the growing tourist traffic into the north since the mid-1980s guarantees further introductions. Indeed, there have been several outbreaks in recent years. Many introductions originate from our closest neighbours, New Guinea and South-East Asia, but they can also come from tropical Africa or South and Central America.

The dengue mosquito, *Aedes aegypti*, is a domestic mosquito that breeds in artificial containers such as gutter puddles and pot-plant saucers, so it's only found around houses. This mosquito often shelters inside houses and generally only bites during daylight hours. Infection with a single strain of dengue causes a fever with debilitating pain in the muscles and joints and behind the eyes. Secondary infection with a different strain of dengue virus can cause a more severe disease known as dengue haemorrhagic fever, which can cause uncontrollable bleeding and death. As there is presently no vaccine, it's important to remove potential mosquito-breeding sites from around houses and screen windows and doors.

Ross River virus disease or Ross River fever
Named for the Ross River in Townsville, north Queensland, where the first case was diagnosed, this Australian virus occurs throughout Australia, including Tasmania. The symptoms of Ross River virus disease are very

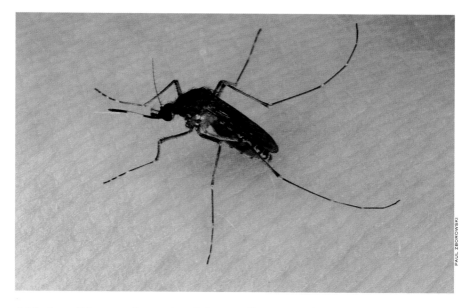

PAUL ZBOROWSKI

A bite from this mosquito species, *Culex annulirostris*, could lead to encephalitis or Ross River fever. The itching reaction caused by a mosquito's bite is the result of saliva injected to prevent the blood from clotting.

variable from person to person and include arthritic pain, lethargy, fever, rash, sore muscles, aching tendons, headaches, sore eyes, sore throat, nausea and tingling. The average duration of symptoms is 6–12 months, although it can vary from two weeks to 10 or more years. It's mainly a disease of adults; if children are affected the symptoms are usually milder and less persistent.

The main vectors of Ross River virus are various *Aedes* mosquitoes although this disease can also be transmitted by *Culex annulirostris*, especially in inland areas. The virus circulates naturally between mosquitoes and wildlife (especially kangaroos and wallabies) and is environmentally driven, being most prevalent in warm, wet conditions. There isn't any prospect of a vaccine in the near future.

Encephalitis

Australian, or Murray Valley, encephalitis occurs in the late wet season in the monsoonal northern areas of WA and the NT. It also occurs as occasional outbreaks in south-eastern Australia following extremely wet summers. Birds help to carry the virus between these areas, and the common banded mosquito, *Culex annulirostris*, can spread it to humans and other mammals. Only one in 1000 of those contracting the virus will develop the disease, but the onset can be life threatening, especially in children. Symptoms include severe headaches, fever, neck stiffness, delirium and an aversion to light. It's a disease affecting the brain, and can result in permanent brain damage in severe cases. In 1995 and 1996, another virus, Japanese encephalitis, was found in the Torres Strait and a single case was reported from mainland Australia early in 1998. This disease is equally dangerous and already common in South-East Asia. In Australia, a vigorous control program is currently underway, involving shooting feral pigs, which can harbour the disease, and hopefully the disease can be contained or eradicated.

Malaria

Malaria is not a viral disease, but a single-celled parasite with a complex life cycle partly completed within mosquitoes. Several species exist throughout the tropics and are transmitted to people by *Anopheles* mosquitoes. Malaria was endemic in Australia but, after a concerted battle, the World Health Organization declared Australia malaria-free in 1981. Many hundreds of cases are still reported every year, but these are contracted overseas. The most telling symptom is a very high fever occurring in daily or longer cycles. Various preventive drugs developed over the past few decades have produced good results, but new strains are emerging that are deadly despite the best medications. The various preventive drugs need to be taken for a set period after returning from a malarial zone, something too many travellers forget.

Prevention

It would be ecologically dangerous – and probably impossible – to eradicate the mosquito species responsible for spreading disease, but vigilance and control of mosquito numbers in populated areas is essential. Unfortunately this is becoming more problematic as insecticide-resistant mosquitoes increase in numbers. The mosquito responsible for transmitting dengue fever is particularly easy for home-owners to control, requiring only the removal of standing water around the house and garden. The use of screens, nets, protective clothing and repellents is important, as parasite and disease cycles can be broken in areas where mosquito bites are drastically reduced.

RON AND VALERIE TAYLOR

A close approach by a large groper can be an intimidating experience for a novice diver but these magnificent creatures rarely bite.

Chapter three

DANGEROUS MARINE ANIMALS

D r   C A R L   E D M O N D S*

My family and I are scuba divers, we love surfing and sailing and are committed to making our ocean adventures as safe and enjoyable as possible. For this reason alone, it's worth knowing about marine animals and how to exist in harmony with them.

There are over 1000 marine vertebrates (animals with backbones) that inject venoms or are poisonous to eat, while the venomous invertebrates are even more numerous but less well known. Many cases of injury involving marine creatures are purely accidental – stepping on a stonefish for example. Some are caused when an animal responds to a perceived threat – a blue-ringed octopus will bite if handled. A very few are the result of deliberate attack, sometimes provoked when a human encroaches on the territory of a marine animal. And even more rarely, injuries occur when a person is seen as prey by an animal such as a shark or crocodile.

Four major groups of dangerous marine creatures are described in this book: marine animals that bite or shock, venomous jellyfish, venomous fish and other venomous animals. The injuries that they can inflict are discussed and appropriate first-aid treatment is suggested. For the health professional, *Dangerous Marine Animals* by Dr Carl Edmonds is recommended as a guide to detailed medical treatment in the event of injury from a marine animal.

As a rule of thumb, the dangerous marine animals can be divided into biters, stingers and poisoners.

Biting is a fairly basic, though highly effective, means of defence and although the number of serious attacks by biting marine animals is very small, speculation, media exploitation and folklore have given them a high profile. Two animals – sharks and crocodiles – are cause for genuine concern, having been responsible for the majority of the fatalities and injuries associated with marine creatures. Marine animals that cause physical trauma, such as the spearing-type injuries and electric shocks of stingrays, can also be grouped with the biters.

The stingers, which include fish and jellyfish, inflict pain or incapacitate their victims with venom – injected by fangs, spines or stinging tentacles – either to obtain food or in self-defence. Some, like the stonefish, hide the venom-delivery system until threatened or attacked, while others, such as the scorpionfish, flaunt lethal-looking appendages or wear gaudy colours to advertise their toxicity, opting for prevention rather than retaliation.

Another strategy is the production of internal toxins that make an animal unpalatable or even lethal to its predators. These animals, and those responsible for some other types of injuries, such as marine infections and allergies, are outside the scope of this book.

Despite this list of marine dangers, bear in mind that, given our national love affair with the sea, the possibility of death or even injury as a result of a run-in with a dangerous marine creature is exceedingly small – we face far greater risks in our day-to-day life. A few simple precautions and a dash of commonsense will allow you to enjoy all the wonders that Australia's fantastic coasts and seas – and the fascinating and beautiful creatures that inhabit them – have to offer.

* Based on text by Dr Carl Edmonds

MARINE ANIMALS THAT BITE OR SHOCK

With such a diverse and spectacular array of predators, it's hardly surprising that the world's oceans contain creatures that are capable of causing injury to people who enter them. Yet the risk of this occurring is often overstated and people's perceptions of it become exaggerated. The most emotive and mythologised predator in the ocean is the shark, but most sharks are harmless and the risk of shark attack is extremely small.

Some of the animals included in this chapter, such as the sharks and crocodiles, are large predators that may view people as prey. Most of the remainder, especially eels and gropers, are often fed by divers and may come to associate people with food, sometimes becoming aggressive when it isn't provided. All of these creatures will bite defensively if they're harassed. Electric rays also possess a defence mechanism in the form of paired organs that can inflict a powerful shock.

Injuries

The typical injuries arising from encounters with most of the species discussed in this chapter involve lacerations. Victims may go into shock, displaying symptoms such as a weak pulse, clammy skin and rapid breathing. Treatment involves techniques for managing blood loss (page 163).

Sharks

Family: Isuridae.
Dangerous species: *Carcharodon carcharias* (white pointer, white death, great white, great white shark).
Family: Carcharhinidae.
Dangerous species: *Galeocerdo cuvier* (tiger shark), *Carcharhinus leucas* (cub, bull, Zambesi or ground shark), *C. longimanus* (oceanic whitetip, white-tipped shark).
Distribution: Most sharks live in relatively shallow coastal waters in temperate or tropical areas. Most are strictly marine, but many will enter estuaries and travel up rivers, and a few inhabit freshwater habitats.

Sharks are superbly adapted hunters, their streamlined bodies glide through the water with fluid grace. In their present-day form they've been around for 100 million years and their origins go back as far as 400–350 mya. They're well equipped to locate prey, relying on a range of extremely accurate senses. For most species the sense of smell is their principal means of finding prey and with it they can detect particular substances, such as blood, in minute quantities – less than one part per million in some cases. Their ability to detect movements in murky water is also highly impressive.

In addition to the other senses, sharks possess an organ called the lateral line, an array of mucous pores along the side. It receives a variety of information, including low-frequency vibrations (a flapping fish for example), pressure and minute electrical fields like those produced by the muscles of fish, seals or even humans in the vicinity.

Although some sharks are known as "dangerous species", this only implies that the species has occasionally – rarely in many cases – been recorded as attacking humans, or has retaliated when people have attacked it or trespassed in its environment. Of the 350–400 known shark species, only 30 have been implicated in attacks on humans. The four species listed above are the only ones responsible for multiple unprovoked attacks. Most sharks 2 m or more in length are potentially dangerous and should be treated with

KEVIN DEACON

Although it's probably the most feared animal in the ocean, the great white shark's biology is still largely a mystery. Hunting pressure has led to it being protected in parts of its range.

respect. A great many more sharks are killed by people than vice versa (around 70 million sharks per year compared to 30 people).

While Australia was for some time regarded as one of the most dangerous areas in the world for shark attack, there is now an average of only one fatality per year. Granted, the risk of attack is genuine, but the possibility of becoming a victim is extremely remote, despite the vast number of bathers potentially at risk. Attacks are more likely at dusk, the shark's natural feeding time; near deep channels; in murky estuaries; and where animal and fish refuse is dumped. Although rare, attacks are often of terrifying intensity, and the degree of injury has a strong emotive effect. Encounters with sharks are commonplace when snorkelling or scuba diving but again, attacks are rare. Many of the recorded attacks have been associated with spearfishing and abalone diving – situations in which vibrations and chemicals from wounded animals are likely to attract sharks.

Several behaviour patterns may precede shark attacks. In some cases the shark circles and occasionally bumps the victim before attacking, presumably to gain some sensory information about an unfamiliar potential food source. Sharks may swim together in a smooth and orderly manner, but when abnormal vibrations are set up, such as when one of the pack is shot or hooked, it can trigger feeding responses in the others that may escalate into a feeding frenzy.

Some tropical species have been known to exhibit a threat display – apparently in response to an intruder in their territory – swimming in an irregular jerking motion with the back arched, head raised and pectoral fins pointing downwards. This abnormal behaviour is a signal to divers to leave the area.

The great white shark often uses a "thump, bite and spit" technique, preferring to strike with great force from below in a single, sudden attack and then retreating until the victim loses consciousness from blood loss. The shark can then feed without fear of damage from a counterattack.

Injuries

The seriousness of a shark-attack injury depends on the size of the shark and the ferocity of the attack. Individuals longer than 2 m have extremely powerful jaws equipped with razor-sharp teeth, and are easily capable of severing limbs or biting large pieces from the torso. Blood loss from such injuries is severe and immediate: major blood vessels are frequently torn, while the tissue laceration leads to generalised bleeding. Victims will display symptoms of severe blood loss such as pale clammy skin, a rapid weak pulse, low blood pressure and rapid respiration and may lose consciousness. Death from a serious attack isn't uncommon. Despite all this, there have been many instances where divers have survived bites from large sharks. In some cases, the divers sustained severe lacerations from the teeth but no further injury. Others have successfully fought their attacker off.

Lessening the risk
● Refrain from spearfishing; vibrations and chemicals given off by speared fish and other injured marine animals commonly attract sharks.
● If you do spearfish, don't carry speared fish close to the body – it invites close inspection by an interested shark.

RON AND VALERIE TAYLOR

The tiger shark isn't a fussy feeder, eating everything from fish and crustaceans to turtles, birds and sea snakes and swallowing a variety of indigestible objects. Such indiscriminate feeding habits make this species dangerous to humans, as does the fact that it can grow to 6 m in length.

- Always dive in company; on statistical grounds alone, this should reduce the likelihood of a shark attack.
- Swim in enclosed or shark-meshed areas when possible.
- Don't swim where shark attacks have occurred recently.
- Avoid swimming at dusk (feeding time for many shark species) or in areas of low visibility.
- Human urine and blood are said to attract sharks.
- In addition to the above precautions, divers should also avoid deep channels and drop-offs.
- If diving among sharks, it's advisable to carry an implement, such as a stick with a metal spike (a shark billy), that can be used to fend them off if necessary.
- Avoid diving near seal colonies.
- Do not handle, touch, grasp or prod sharks, even small ones. Several species can twist suddenly and give a nasty bite.

Crocodiles

Family: Crocodylidae.

Dangerous species: *Crocodylus porosus* (saltwater or estuarine crocodile), *C. johnstoni* (freshwater or Johnston River crocodile).

Distribution: The saltwater crocodile has a wide distribution including the tropics and subtropics of Australia, the Indo-Pacific islands and eastern India. The freshwater crocodile is restricted to Australia's northern waterways from Cape York to the Kimberley.

Saltwater crocodile

Freshwater crocodile

The crocodilians (including crocodiles, alligators and caimans) are survivors from the dinosaur age, over 65 mya. Crocodiles are carnivorous and tend to be opportunistic feeders, their diet depending on what sort of food is available and the size of the crocodile; juveniles feed mainly on insects, while adults take larger prey such as birds and mammals.

Crocodiles have quite complex brains and are intelligent enough to stalk a human, strong enough to overpower a water buffalo, and gentle enough to carry their hatchlings in their massive jaws. They have a highly developed social life, exhibit individual recognition, territoriality, complex courtship behaviours and communicate vocally by grunts and growls, chemically by secretions from glands in the cloaca and chin and behaviourally by body postures and movements. They become more aggressive during the breeding season. The female remains at the nest after she's laid her eggs, defending it from predators and digging out her offspring when they hatch (their calls alert her). She remains with the young for some time and will respond quickly and aggressively to their distress calls. The sex of the hatchlings is determined by the temperature of the nest: if it's around 32°C hatchlings will be male; below 31°C or above 33°C and they'll be female.

ROBBI NEWMAN

When hunting, saltwater crocodiles rely on their camouflage to allow them to sneak up on their prey before erupting from the water in a short, fast, powerful lunge.

Crocodiles often lie in the water along the banks of rivers, only the ears, nostrils and eyes protruding above the surface. Prey, especially a land animal that comes to the riverbank to drink, may be grabbed suddenly in the crocodile's immensely strong jaws and twisted off its feet; once the prey is in the water it's more vulnerable to panic and drowning. Although large crocodiles rarely venture out of the water, attacks have been recorded on land. Out of the water, crocodiles are capable of short bursts of rapid movement over a short distance, and will sometimes sweep the victim off its feet with the powerful tail. Attacks on land occur most frequently at night, the time when the animal commonly stalks its food.

The species responsible for fatal attacks on humans is the saltwater crocodile, which has been known to grow to more than 7 m in length and a tonne in weight (although the average maximum size for a male is closer to 5 m). Its name is somewhat misleading as it's most commonly found in freshwater and estuarine environments; so there is no guarantee that a crocodile encountered in fresh water is a freshwater crocodile. The freshwater crocodile, most commonly found in billabongs and rivers away from the sea,

The long narrow snout and smaller size of the freshwater crocodile distinguishes it from the more dangerous saltwater variety.

can be distinguished by its thinner snout and smaller size. Bites from this species have been recorded, but unprovoked attacks are exceedingly rare and all of the lethal attacks have been attributed to saltwater crocodiles.

Since the mid-1970s, conservation practices have resulted in an increase both in population and average size of crocodiles. This has had some unfortunate consequences: as the animals grow older, larger, and more numerous, conflicts with humans become more frequent and potentially more dangerous. However, the number of attacks is still low and "problem" crocodiles are routinely and efficiently removed when they threaten safety. Over the past 27 years there have been 38 attacks by saltwater crocodiles in Australia. Fourteen of these were fatal, an average of only 0.5 fatal attacks per year.

Lessening the risk

- Pay close attention to local warnings and signposts.
- Check with local authorities before venturing into "crocodile country".
- Don't wade, swim, stand or canoe in tropical waterways and estuaries, or walk along, fish from or camp on their banks.
- An attack may sometimes be thwarted by retaliation, such as hitting the crocodile's snout or gouging its eyes.
- Alcohol has been a factor in a high proportion of crocodile attacks and its consumption in areas where crocodiles are present should be minimised.

Eels

Families: Muraenidae, Leptocephalidae.
Dangerous species: *Gymnothorax javanicus*
(giant moray), *G. meleagris* (whitemouth moray,
tropical moray), *Conger labiatus* (conger eel)
and others.
Distribution: Tropical, subtropical and
temperate waters.

The moray eel's fearsome reputation is due more to its appearance than to its behaviour. The bead-like eyes seem capable of transfixing a potential victim and the open mouth, armed with a fearsome array of teeth, appears ever ready to bite. In fact, the mouth is open so that water can pass over the animal's gills, allowing it to breathe.

Although usually nocturnal, moray eels can often be seen during the day, head poking from a hole or crevice. They grow to 2.5 m in length and 30 cm in diameter and most are attractively marked with spots and other patterns. Feeding mostly on fish and invertebrates, moray eels rarely attack without cause but can be provoked by intrusion into their territory or on being injured or caught.

Conger eels, on the other hand, have a reputation for possessing a vicious disposition. Exceptional specimens may grow to 3 m in length and 40 kg in weight, but frequently they are in the 1 m/10 kg range. Their colour varies from black to brownish yellow, with a purple tinge and a pale underside. Freshwater eels have also been known to attack and bite humans but have poorly developed teeth. Sea snakes are sometimes mistaken for eels, but they can be readily identified by the flat paddle-shaped tail, scales, and need to surface regularly to breathe.

Morays can be tamed by divers and fed with cut urchins, sausages or pieces of fish. Many dive resorts have their own "pet" morays, which unfortunately learn to equate divers with food and may become aggressive when it isn't supplied. Although usually encountered in their lairs, eels can attack in open water – behaviour that I never witnessed in my earlier diving years, but which now occurs frequently where eels are fed. Attacks occur when divers wave their hands, the eel is speared, or surfers dangle feet or hands over their boards.

RON AND VALERIE TAYLOR

Yellowmargin moray eels grow to more than a metre. They are easily tamed, quickly becoming accustomed to the presence of divers; however, feeding them can result in attacks later, when food isn't offered.

The upper teeth are hinged and when not in use may lie flat, pointing backwards. The muscular jaws can clamp with great power, and the eel tears the flesh from its prey by winding its tail into a knot and slipping the knot down the body of the prey until it reaches the eel's head. The eel then uses this support to prise off the meat. If they do attack, they are very awkward to grasp and difficult to dislodge, and even then may resume the attack.

Injuries

Wounds from eel bites are usually torn and ragged with profuse bleeding, and secondary infection is common. It's been claimed that bites may include a venom that causes local paralysis, but this hasn't been well documented.

If blood loss is severe the patient may go into shock, the symptoms of which include a sweaty (cold and clammy) appearance, rapid pulse, a dramatic decrease in blood pressure (hypotension) and syncope (fainting) on standing.

Lessening the risk

- Do not spear eels.
- Do not intrude into their habitat.
- Do not feed them.
- Wear heavy protective clothing (boots, gloves) when handling eels caught on lines.
- Wear thick gloves when diving in likely eel habitat.

Electric rays

Family: Torpedinidae.

Dangerous species: *Hypnos monopterygium,*
Torpedo macneilli, Narcine tasmaniensis
and others.

Common names: Numb ray, numbfish,
torpedo ray, coffin ray.

Distribution: Temperate coastlines.

Electric rays are slow and ineffective swimmers, and usually lie submerged in mud or sand with only the nostrils visible, sometimes in quite shallow water. The thick, kidney-shaped electric organs – which automatically discharge an electric current if touched – are usually discernible on each side of the spinal column. It isn't necessary to have direct contact with the body of the ray for a shock to be felt. The discharge varies from 8 to 220 volts, and is passed between the electrically negative underside of the ray to the electrically positive topside. The ray can deliver a series of successive discharges with lessening intensity, followed by a latent period during which it recharges its electric potential.

Injuries

On rare occasions the electric shock will temporarily disable the victim, which could lead to drowning. In such cases cardio-pulmonary resuscitation will be necessary (page 158). It's more common for shocks to occur on land or on boats when rays are caught on lines or in trawls. In these cases injuries may occur when the victim falls after being shocked. Shocks don't usually have any visible effects and recovery is achieved without treatment.

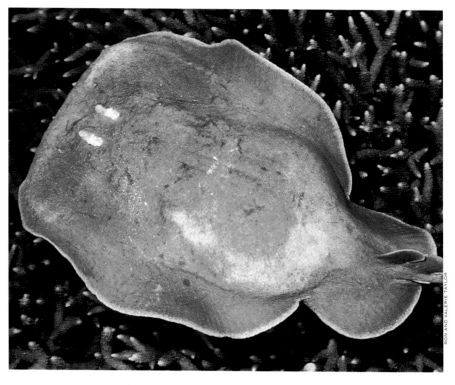

The coffin ray is capable of producing a shock strong enough to be felt through a stream of water poured onto its back. A slow moving fish, it uses its electric organs to stun prey such as crabs, worms and small fishes.

Gropers

Family: Serranidae.
Dangerous species: *Plectropomus* spp.,
Epinephelus spp., *Polyprion* spp. and others.
Common names: Grouper/groper, giant cod,
spotted cod, sea bass, cod.
Distribution: Tropical, subtropical and
temperate waters.

Gropers are the heavyweights of the sea: the Queensland groper is the world's biggest reef-dwelling fish, the larger specimens on the Great Barrier Reef (GBR) reaching 3 m in length and 100–200 kilograms in weight. Sometimes becoming quite tame, they live in wrecks, caves and coral caverns protected by overhangs and, being very curious, are often photographed. Once they appreciate that divers can be a source of food, gropers will often remain in an area and approach all humans, causing apprehension in those unaccustomed to their "friendliness".

Waving hands and feet can simulate the activity of fish and may attract a groper's attention – the cause of most minor groper-related injuries – the hand or foot being spat out when the fish is unable to swallow it. Gropers swallow most of their food, mainly other fish, whole; their powerful jaws contain broad bands of small pointed teeth and are designed for gaining a firm hold on prey rather than tearing it apart.

Although usually quite friendly to divers, gropers may become aggressive if they've been fed. Some species can grow to 3 m in length and their powerful jaws, huge mouths and small pointed teeth are capable of inflicting serious damage. Unprovoked attacks do occasionally occur and in some areas gropers are more feared than sharks.

RON AND VALERIE TAYLOR

Unprovoked attacks on swimmers and divers have also been reported, and in some areas, such as Torres Strait, gropers are more feared than sharks. They've been known to grab hands, feet, even the bodies of divers and surfers, amply verifying their potential to cause injury. Fatalities have been described, although they are rare and poorly documented. The only case I know of is that of a small Queensland girl.

Injuries

Groper wounds are generally ragged, with extensive tissue laceration and profuse bleeding. Secondary infection is common and should be guarded against. Victims of a severe attack may lapse into shock, becoming pale and sweaty (cold, clammy) with a rapid pulse and hypotension (abnormally low blood pressure). Fainting on standing may be due to blood loss. First aid is as for shark attack (page 163).

Lessening the risk

- Try to avoid entering the realm of a territorial groper.
- Avoid handling speared fish underwater and carry them held well away from the body.
- Scare techniques used by divers against sharks, such as blowing bubbles, making a noise or moving forward, are of no use against gropers.

Octopuses

Class: Cephalopoda.
Order: Octopoda.
Dangerous species: *Octopus hongkongensis, O. vulgaris* and others.
Distribution: All oceans.

The octopus is an eight-armed mollusc, related to squid, cuttlefish and garden snails among others. It inhabits all the world's oceans from the Arctic to the Antarctic, from the surface waters to depths of 5000 m. The largest known species is *Octopus hongkongensis* of the Pacific which has an arm span of up to 9.5 m. The common octopus, *O. vulgaris*, is found in tropical and temperate waters and can have an arm span of 3 m and weigh more than 22 kg.

The octopus has a beak capable of piercing shellfish, suction pads that are strong enough to prise open bivalves and oysters, and defensive sepia or ink, which it can discharge a number of times in rapid succession. This sepia can be used as a "smokescreen", a threat display or as a decoy to distract and confuse predators by creating a scent similar to that of the octopus itself. A moray, shark or groper could waste valuable time attacking the ink cloud, allowing the octopus to escape. Venom from the salivary glands can be injected directly into a bite or into the seawater surrounding a small victim. This venom contains enzymes and toxins that are especially toxic to crabs and vary from one octopus species to another.

Octopuses use their powerful beaks to pierce the shells of their prey, mainly clams, crabs and snails. In some species females can produce more than 500,000 eggs and many guard them until they hatch.

GERRY ALLEN

By far the most common popular image of octopus attack is that of the creature fixing itself to an undersea object while holding a diver with the suckers on its other arms. It's tempting to write this off as Hollywood licence were it not for reports by some divers who can be considered reasonably credible. There have been reported incidents of octopuses attacking divers, occasionally unprovoked, but more often than not retaliating against a spear- or knife-thrust.

As most swimmers frequent beaches with sandy bottoms, they are unlikely to encounter octopuses as this environment offers little or no shelter for these animals. Divers on the other hand frequent reefs, corals and rocky areas – ideal octopus habitat.

Injuries

An octopus bite gives rise to a variety of symptoms in humans, sometimes causing pain very quickly. At other times a severe tissue reaction or inflammation with gross swelling and numbness occurs. It may take many days to diminish, and often produces itching.

Bites from octopuses are rare; a review published in 1971 could find only nine reports of octopus bites other than those of the deadly blue-ringed octopus (page 139).

Part II

JELLYFISH
AND THEIR KIN

There are around 9000 known species of cnidarian (also known as coelenterates) including, among others, jellyfish, sea anemones, corals, fire corals and stinging hydroids. Although some look like flowers and others like ferns, they are all carnivorous animals. Free-swimming jellyfish inhabit all of the oceans, but are most diverse and abundant in a belt covering the area between latitudes 45°N and 30°S, although some species' ranges occasionally extend into Arctic and Antarctic waters. Attached cnidarians, such as anemones and corals, have a wide distribution but are most abundant in the shallow (less than 30 m) warm waters of the tropics and subtropics.

All cnidarians have one thing in common – stinging cells or nematocysts, the cause of all injuries associated with these animals. It's this unique feature that gives the group its name, from a Greek word for nettle. These cells consist of a fluid-filled capsule containing a coiled thread. The thread is shot out when the cell is stimulated, adhering to the prey either by a sticky substance or a hook. During discharge the nematocyst thread can act like a hypodermic needle, piercing the prey and injecting any venom stored in the thread or capsule. This firing of the nematocyst is triggered by many factors, including injury or disturbance to the cnidarian, but its main function is to immobilise prey so that it can be eaten.

The severity and type of injuries caused by cnidarians depends on the number of nematocysts that fire into the victim. This in turn is related to the length and number of tentacles and the density of nematocysts on the tentacles. The box jellyfish, with as many as 50 tentacles, produces multiple, long red weals on human skin and the tentacles often adhere through the combination of a sticky substance exuded by the nematocysts and the hooks of the nematocysts themselves. The Portuguese man-o'-war, on the other hand, with one main tentacle, usually produces a single long straplike mark with small blisters along the skin.

Fire corals, sea anemones and stinging hydroids, being non-mobile, sting only when brushed against. They spend most of their adult life attached to underwater objects such as rocks and reefs and the nematocysts in their tentacles are mostly used to capture food – usually passing plankton.

Injuries

Cnidarian venom consists of chemicals and enzymes that affect cell membranes, causing injury to the skin, muscles, heart, brain and nerves. Symptoms may vary from a mild local itch to severe reaction and even death.

Skin reactions may be local, often occurring as a mild prickly sensation that develops immediately upon contact. In other cases, a severe burning or throbbing pain may develop and may be associated with local sweating, scarring, and/or death of underlying tissue. Patients may also exhibit sores that appear after a delay of 5–30 days. These may be recurring and can appear at a distance from the original sting. For the more common immediate sting, intensity increases over a few minutes and the red, inflamed area may develop blisters or, in severe cases, ulcers. The pain may spread to involve the lymph glands and can cause abdominal and chest pain.

Generalised symptoms include fever, sweating, gastrointestinal disorders, heart failure, difficulty breathing and the victim becoming confused or delirious. Psychological symptoms caused by the neurological effects of the sting, such as anxiety, depression, insomnia, weakness and apathy, may follow. Sub-acute or chronic complications, such as damage to the peripheral nerves or vascular system have been described.

The intensity of the symptoms varies according to:
- the species involved (the box jellyfish may be lethal, whereas the blubber jellyfish can often be handled without problems);
- the extent of the contact area;
- the thickness of the skin at the point of contact;
- the maturity of the animal;
- the body weight of the victim (stings will be more severe in children than adults);

- individual factors such as allergic reactions and pre-existing cardiac or respiratory disease.

Variations in the type of injury can be influenced by other injuries and allergic or anaphylactic (hypersensitive) reactions. For complications caused by allergies and anaphylaxis, see page 183.

➕ **For first aid see page 174.**

Portuguese man-o'-war

Order: Siphonophora.
Family: Physaliidae.
Dangerous species: *Physalia physalis (utriculus).*
Common names: Portuguese man-o'-war, bluebottle, physalia.
Distribution: Most tropical, subtropical and temperate waters. More prevalent in summer months in cooler regions.

Each Portuguese man-o'-war is actually a colony of organisms. The large gas-filled, transparent sac, usually blue coloured and a few centimetres long, is called a pneumatophore and allows the Portuguese man-o'-war to float. Attached to the pneumatophore are feeding polyps, reproductive zooids and one or more long "fishing" tentacles, which may extend for as much as 10 m and are used to capture food, mainly plankton and small fish. When the tentacles come into contact with prey, they contract and discharge numerous nematocysts, thereby paralysing it. The fishing tentacle is then retracted so that the feeding polyps can digest the food.

Large numbers of Portuguese men-o'-war are often blown onto beaches by onshore winds, where children delight in popping them – often with unpleasant consequences, for the nematocysts may remain potent even after death. Deaths from Portuguese man-o'-war stings are rare but have been recorded. Many victims brought in to the hospitals near Sydney's beaches have required resuscitation. The injury is usually a single, long, whip-like strip of inflamed skin.

HOWARD PLOWMAN/NATURE FOCUS

Portuguese men-o'-war are usually found in open water but when onshore winds blow they can be stranded on beaches in their hundreds. They should still be avoided as they can sting for some time after being beached.

Lessening the risk

● Do not touch these creatures, even if they are lying on the sand.

● Use protective clothing when in the water.

● Remain out of the water when Portuguese men-o'-war are present.

● Be aware of onshore winds – there may be large numbers of the animals present in the water two days or more after the winds cease blowing.

Box jellyfish

Order: Cubomedusae.
Family: Chirodropidae.
Dangerous species: *Chironex fleckeri*.
Common names: Chironex, deadly sea wasp, sea wasp, fire medusa, indringa, Flecker's box-jelly.
Distribution: Restricted to the warm waters of the Indian and Pacific oceans.

In northern Australia this deadly stinging creature is encountered from spring to autumn, and the 70 or more box jellyfish fatalities in Australian waters have all occurred between the months of October and May. It, or similar species, may occur in other months if seasonal conditions permit, and in waters north of Australia including those of Papua New Guinea, Indonesia, the Philippines and Malaysia. The box jellyfish is an active swimmer and may be present even in very shallow water off beaches. The immature forms grow in estuaries and around mangroves.

Its numerous tentacles, attached at four corners, may trail up to 3 m behind the body. The tentacles cling to the victim's skin and contain thousands of nematocysts, which inject tiny doses of venom into the victim. These innumerable tiny doses combine into a large volume of deadly toxin, the amount depending on the length of tentacle in contact with the victim, the area stung, and the thickness of the skin.

The venom has its most serious effects on the heart and the respiratory system, with death usually being due to paralysis of the respiratory muscles. Its effects on the heart – weakening the contractions and interfering with its rhythm – compound the problem. The venom also causes agonising localised pain.

Injuries

The victim experiences immediate agonising pain on contact with the tentacles, the injuries consisting of multiple, interlacing lines. In the case of a large sting, sudden collapse, cessation of breathing, a bluish tinge to the skin (cyanosis), loss of consciousness and death may follow rapidly. The effects are particularly dangerous for small children and elderly or frail swimmers. In non-lethal cases, severe pain persists for many hours and scarring caused by local tissue destruction is common at the sting site.

➕ **For first aid see page 174.**

CASE REPORT. My first exposure to the aftermath of a box jellyfish sting occurred in 1962 when I was working as the flying doctor in Derby, WA. A young man dived into the ocean and almost immediately rose to the surface, screaming in agony. Two bystanders who rushed to his aid were also stung by the sticky tentacles that had wrapped themselves around his body but they managed to drag him to the shore, pulling the tentacles off him at the same time.

In a state ranging from unconsciousness to extreme agitation, the man was transferred to hospital where administration of morphine and pethidine failed to relieve the obvious agony he was experiencing. As we failed to recognise the specific problem at the time (this was before I researched my first text on marine animal injuries), we anaesthetised the patient and kept him unconscious until we were able to reduce the anaesthesia without a recurrence of the severe distress. This type of treatment certainly wouldn't be recommended nowadays, but it worked at the time.

Each year between October and May the beaches of northern Australia are off-limits to swimmers due to the arrival of the box jellyfish, one of the world's most lethal jellyfish.

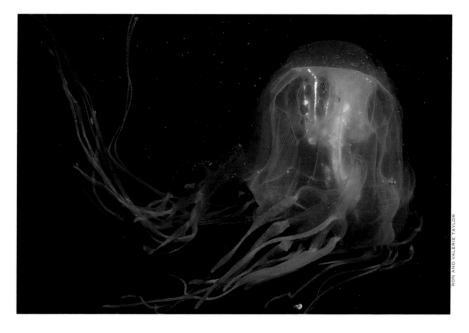

RON AND VALERIE TAYLOR

Lessening the risk

- Avoid swimming in northern Australian waters during the box jellyfish season (October–May). Special areas enclosed by fine mesh netting may permit safe swimming.
- The animal often can't be seen from the surface, so avoid jumping from boats or jetties into the water.
- Cover as much exposed skin as possible by wearing a face mask, wet suit and hood or a Lycra suit while swimming. This prevents the tentacles coming in contact with the skin and also reduces the risk of stings from other jellyfish and injuries from corals.

Sea wasp variants

Families: Chirodropidae and Carybdeidae.
Dangerous species: *Chiropsalmus* spp., *Tamoya* spp.,
Carybdea spp., *Morbakka* spp. and others.
Common names: Sea wasps, box jellyfish.
Distribution: Tropical and temperate waters.

The box jellyfish isn't the only member of the family Chirodropidae that's capable of inflicting intense pain and even causing death. These jellyfish, along with some members of the family Carybdeidae, are also often referred to as sea wasps. Some, in common with the box jellyfish, have multiple tentacles on the four corners, although the body is generally smaller and the tentacles fewer and smaller, while others have a single thick tentacle on each corner. They also share a similar tropical distribution with the box jellyfish. These species have been implicated in deaths in the Philippines. There is a possibility that the box jellyfish antivenom may be effective against stings of one of these genera, *Chiropsalmus*.

Although the name "sea wasp" is used somewhat indiscriminately, it does serve to accentuate the importance of some of their stings. In the Australasian region, the term sea wasp is often considered synonymous with death – even though most victims survive. Treatment of such stings is based on the same general principles as those described for the box jellyfish and other jellyfish on page 174.

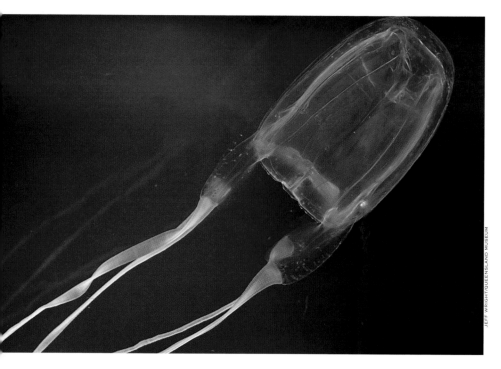

As its name suggests, the Moreton Bay box jellyfish occurs in southern Queensland waters. Like the other sea wasps, this species is most common in summer. Its sting is extremely painful but not lethal.

Irukandji

Family: Carybdeidae.

Dangerous species: *Carukia barnesi* and others.

Common names: Box jellyfish, type-A stinging jellyfish.

Distribution: Tropical waters along the eastern and western coasts of Australia, and occasionally around the islands of the Indian and Pacific oceans (including Indonesia and Fiji). Their distribution may be much wider.

Symptoms resulting from Irukandji stings have at times been confused with those of appendicitis or a ruptured gastric ulcer, partly because the sting causes more generalised symptoms than a simple local injury.

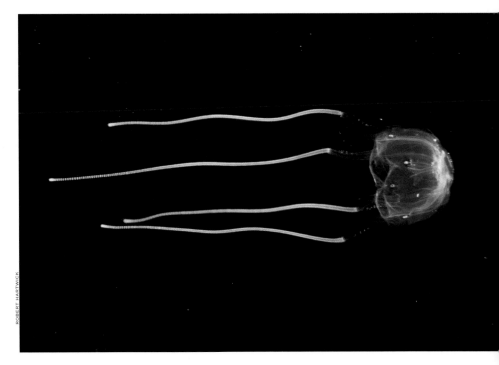

ROBERT HARTWICK

The Irukandji usually appears in swarms off the east and west tropical coasts during summer. Stinging cells are present on the bell as well as the tentacles and stings often appear as an oblong skin reaction.

The Irukandji – a small box jellyfish with a transparent body about 1–2 cm long and four tentacles varying from 5 cm to 1 m in length, depending on the degree of contraction – was named after an Aboriginal community near Cairns, where the symptoms were first described. However, similar clinical symptoms may accompany stings from other cnidarians mentioned in this book.

This animal is rarely observed by the victim, even though a sting usually occurs near the surface and in shallow water. Stingings typically occur in coastal areas, often in late summer, while others occur further out to sea in depths of 10–20 m, the injury varying with the duration, extent and site of the sting. The pearl divers of WA are often affected by Irukandji.

Injuries

A few seconds after contact, the victim may feel a stinging sensation, which can increase in intensity for a few minutes and then diminish. It may be sufficient to cause children to cry and adults to leave the water.

A red-coloured reaction, 5–7 cm in diameter, surrounds the area of contact within five minutes. Small papules (pimples) appear and reach their maximum size after 20 minutes, before subsiding. The red colour can occasionally last up to three hours and there may be excessive sweating over the area.

There's usually a latent period of 5–120 minutes between contact and the development of generalised symptoms and the patient may not realise the relationship between the two. The patient experiences severe abdominal pains, often coming in waves, muscular aches such as cramps and dull, drill-like pains, accompanied by muscle tenderness. Profuse sweating, anxiety and restlessness may develop, as may nausea and vomiting. Respiratory distress with coughing and grunting may occur and there may be an increased blood pressure and pulse rate, with cardiac irregularities.

Later symptoms include numbness and tingling, itching, smarting eyes, sneezing, joint and nerve pains, weakness, rigors, dry mouth and headache. All symptoms should diminish or cease within 4–12 hours. Occasionally discomfort and distress may persist and convalescence may take up to a week.

Jimble

Family: Carybdeidae.
Dangerous species: *Carybdea rastoni* and others.
Common names: Small box jellyfish, lantern medusa, mona, sea wasp (USA).
Distribution: Indian, Pacific and Atlantic oceans, in both tropical and temperate areas, especially during the change of seasons.

The jimble looks like the Irukandji. It tends to rise towards the surface during the early morning and evening, or on cloudy days, and is sometimes difficult to identify in the water. It's especially common during spring, occurring in swarms in sheltered waters such as those of Sydney Harbour. Jimbles will cause injury if they touch the sensitive skin of children or areas such as the forearm and are best handled using gloves.

Symptoms associated with a jimble sting are often more severe than those caused by Portuguese men-o'-war, and a sting can cause permanent scarring. Like the Irukandji it has four tentacles, which will produce two to four short, red lines on contact with sensitive skin. In some cases a sting will be as painful and as clinically serious as that of the "sea wasp variants" (page 113).

Like other jellyfish, the jimble is carnivorous, feeding mostly on small fish, which are captured by the tentacles and then drawn up into the bell to be digested. The tentacles are sometimes pink and are usually seen before the transparent bell. An active swimmer, this denizen of coastal waters spends much of the day close to the seabed, rising to the surface in the morning and evening and on cloudy days.

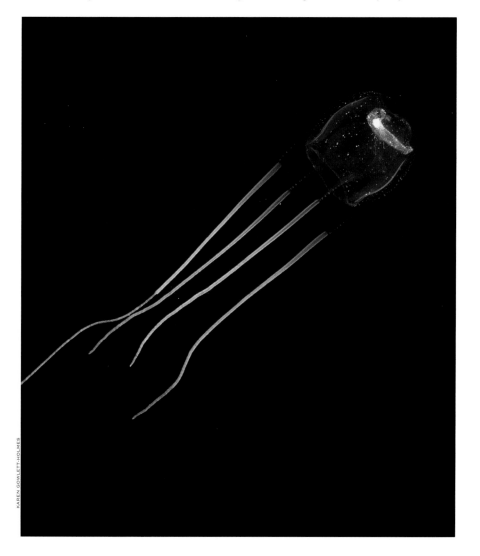

KAREN GOWLETT-HOLMES

Miscellaneous jellyfish, nettles and "sea lice"

Orders: Semaeostomeae, Rhizostomeae.
Dangerous species: *Aurelia aurita,*
Chrysaora quinquecirra, Leuckartiara gardineri,
Olindias singularis and others.
Common names: Moon jelly, saucer blubber,
stinging nettle, yaringa, noko.

Blubber jellyfish
Dangerous species: *Catostylus mosaicus,*
Rhizostoma pulmo, R. cuvieri.
Common names: Man-o'-war, blubber, brown
blubber, German blubber, jelly blubber.

Cyanea
Dangerous species: *Cyanea capillata, C. annaskala,*
C. arctica, C. nozakii and others.
Common names: Sea blubber, hairy stinger, sea
nettle, hairy jelly, lion's mane, malonga, snotty.

Mauve stinger
Dangerous species: *Pelagia noctiluca.*
Common names: Mauve blubber, augas vivas,
quallen, purple stinger.

Distribution: Worldwide.

Many jellyfish have nematocysts capable of piercing human skin. As a general rule, the more mature the cnidarian, the more severe the sting. A sting's severity will also depend on the part of the body stung – the soft skin of a child, or the inside of the forearm and thigh will be more severely affected than the tougher palms of hands or soles of feet.

Blubber jellyfish have a dome-shaped bell, which may be up to 30 cm in diameter and 8 cm thick, trailing tentacles capable of inflicting stings. They vary in colour according to season and location. They can often, but not

The stinging abilities of many jellyfish species remain poorly known. It's always best to assume that a jellyfish will sting and leave it alone.

always, be handled with impunity, their stinging ability varying at different times of the year, being more potent during the breeding season.

The mauve stinger only grows to about 13 cm across the bell but has eight tentacles that may be more than 1 m in length. Although generally mauve or purple, it may be dark brown or red. Nematocysts are present not only on the tentacles but also on the warty upper surface of the bell.

Cyanea are red or yellow, umbrella-shaped jellyfish, which are most numerous during summer and may be up to a metre across. The tentacles –

The lion's mane or hair jelly can grow to an impressive size, its tentacles occasionally reaching 2 m in length. Unlike the sea wasps, it is most commonly observed during winter when most swimmers are wearing wetsuits so stingings are infrequent. Although its sting is usually relatively painless, large specimens are potentially dangerous.

KEVIN DEACON

which can be up to 10 m long – are easily damaged and may separate from the body, rendering the animal harmless.

Nematocysts are capable of firing even after the death of the jellyfish that bears them. Tentacles are often broken up in surf after the animal dies, causing small pieces, still armed with their battery of nematocysts, to be scattered throughout the water. When this happens, many swimmers may be stung over wide areas of the body by these so-called "sea lice".

In general, the term sea lice refers to some indeterminate cause of a rash that develops after swimming in the ocean. Sometimes *Glaucus,* a 1–3 cm long blue and white mollusc, will be referred to as sea lice. *Glaucus* feeds on floating jellyfish, collecting their nematocysts for its own use and so the severity of its sting depends on the type of jellyfish eaten. Other sea-lice candidates include free-swimming mini-crustaceans such as cymothoids, cirolanids and some algae.

Injuries

Usually a minor irritation or sting that may intensify if the site is rubbed or scratched and appear as a blotchy red patch in which a blistered weal may form. The weal may increase for a few minutes and then diminish over the next hour. Pain may precede or parallel the appearance of the lesion and may extend to regional lymph nodes. In the event of an extensive sting, general symptoms, such as those described on page 116, may occur; however, they will normally fade within an hour or two.

CASE REPORT. During a conference of diving doctors in the West Indies in 1984, most of the participants and their partners were stung by numerous small, broken cnidarian tentacles and were in considerable discomfort. Heated discussion about the best treatment followed, and various methods were tried.

Vinegar was found to be totally ineffectual, and other treatments almost so. Then an elderly woman offered the use of her tannic acid spray – it worked immediately.

One possible explanation for its effectiveness was that it contained not only tannic acid, but coolants, local anaesthetic, volatile alcohols and many other chemicals.

Fire corals

Class: Hydrozoa.

Dangerous species: *Millepora* spp.

Common names: Stinging coral, false coral, karang gatal (itchy corals).

Distribution: Tropical and subtropical waters, or where the water is warm, such as around the outlets of power stations.

These animals are called corals because of their similarity in appearance to the reef-building true corals. They occur in many different sizes, shapes and colours but all have a skeletal covering pitted by many tiny pores – hence the generic name *Millepora* – through which nematocyst-bearing tentacles project.

Accidentally brushing against these tentacles has caused unexpected pain to many a snorkeller or diver. The sting is more severe on delicate skin and increases with the area of exposure.

Fire corals can be difficult to distinguish from other, harmless varieties. The best advice is to wear protective swimwear when snorkelling or diving on coral reefs and to avoid touching any of the reef's inhabitants.

Sea anemones

Class: Anthozoa.

Dangerous species: *Actinia* spp., *Actinodendron* spp., *Adamsia* spp., *Alicia* spp., *Anemonia* spp., *Calliactis* spp., *Lebrunia* spp., *Physobrachia* spp., *Rhodactis* spp., *Sagartia* spp., *Telmatactis* spp.

Common names: Stinging anemone, actinarian, hell's fire, lumane, matalelei.

Distribution: Tropical, subtropical and temperate waters.

The attractive colours of many anemones and their tendency to remain anchored in one position make them a magnet for children and collectors, who may suffer unexpected consequences. They often live at, or below, the low-water mark, and have a covering of sticky material that aids adherence of the nematocysts to the victim.

On coral reefs, many anemones are inhabited by anemonefish – brightly coloured animals that have entered into a symbiotic relationship with the cnidarians. The anemonefish secrete a special mucus that stops the anemone's nematocysts from firing.

RON AND VALERIE TAYLOR

Stinging hydroids

Family: Plumulariidae.

Dangerous species: *Aglaophenia* spp., *Lytocarpus* spp.

Common names: Stinging seaweed, fire weed, fire fern, feather hydroid.

Distribution: Tropical and subtropical regions, and where there are warm waters and shallow reefs.

Although this fern-like organism looks like seaweed, it's an animal with a powerful sting. Living attached to rocks, many are found in areas where a surge or current washes the plankton on which they feed close enough for their polyps to catch. Stinging hydroids come in a variety of colours from brownish green to purple to white. They grow on reefs and in warm waters, such as those around power-station outlets. Their effects on humans are highly variable. On some occasions they can be handled without effect, while at other times handling can result in extreme pain. It's best to treat all hydroids as if they can deliver a painful sting.

The largest stinging hydroid in the tropics, the cypress sea fern grows to a metre in height. It is named for its resemblance to the fronds of a cypress tree.

Part III

VENOMOUS FISH

Venomous fish deliver their toxins through sharp spines, using them for defence rather than attack. The spines may be concealed, only becoming obvious when in use, as is true of the stonefish, or displayed conspicuously as a warning to predators, as with butterfly cod. The venoms that some of these fish possess are potentially lethal, while others cause only local reactions. Stings can occur even after a fish has died.

As a general rule, fish that have been damaged, in a fishing net for example, are less likely to deliver a sting, probably because the envenomation system has already been triggered or damaged. When a wound from a fish spine bleeds profusely it's also less likely to have intense symptoms, probably due to the flushing or dilution of venom with the blood. Some fish spines aren't connected to venom sacs and therefore produce few symptoms.

General symptoms of fish stings such as shock, respiratory depression and death occur when the venom enters and disperses through the body. It follows that the victim's body weight is a major factor in the severity of the symptoms: children, therefore, are at greater risk than adults. The physical health of the victim is also relevant, and conditions such as asthma and coronary artery disease may increase the chance that a sting will be fatal.

Other fish produce cutting injuries with knife-like spines that may or may not result in envenomation. In many cases, a slime exists on the spines that may contribute as greatly to inflammation and infections as any venom.

The site of the wound, the number of punctures and their pattern will help identify the fish that caused the injury. Fortunately there is generally little variation in the symptoms of the various fish stings, although the severity may vary greatly, both between and within species.

Injuries

The victim experiences immediate local pain – increasing in intensity over a few minutes – which may become excruciating but usually lessens after a few hours for an average sting. Old-timers say that it lasts "until the turn of the tide".

The puncture wound will have a blanched rim with a red, inflamed and sometimes bluish zone and the area around it becomes pale and swollen within half an hour. The swelling is worsened by activity but can be partially alleviated by elevating the injured area. The puncture wounds become numb, but the area surrounding them will be hypersensitive, and pain and tenderness may develop in the lymph glands of the groin or armpit. Paralysis of the surrounding muscles is common.

In addition to the local symptoms, potentially severe generalised symptoms may be experienced. The patient is often very distressed by the degree of pain and this distress may cause him or her to become delirious. In severe cases the victim may develop respiratory distress and/or a state of cardiovascular shock that may result in death.

After recovery from the acute phase of a serious fish sting, psychological symptoms deriving from the neurological effects of the sting including anxiety, apathy, weakness, impaired concentration, insomnia and depression are not uncommon and may last for days or months. Other delayed complications include a recurrence of the inflammation around the sting one to three weeks later. This may be due either to a reaction to a foreign body remaining in the wound, or to a secondary infection.

✚ **For first aid see page 175.**

Stonefishes

Family: Scorpaenidae.

Dangerous species: *Synanceja verrucosa,*
S. trachynis, S. horrida.

Common names: Dornorn, rockfish, goblinfish, nofu
("the waiting one"), devil fish, warty-ghoul,
deadly stonefish.

Distribution: Indian and Pacific oceans. Many
similar species are found in other tropical areas.

KEVIN DEACON

Like other stonefishes, the reef stonefish spends most of its time sitting motionless on the seafloor waiting to ambush prey – crustaceans and small fish – as it swims past.

The stonefish is among the most poisonous fish known. Covered everywhere, even at the tips of its spines, by loose mottled skin, the fish is perfectly camouflaged and grows to about 30 cm in length, but can be larger. It can burrow under sand and mud with its large pectoral fins and often lies in shallow water. The stonefish can also survive many hours out of water if stranded on a reef at low tide. At greater depths it's easier to recognise because of its bulk and floppy swimming style.

The 13 spines on its back – which are capable of piercing a rubber-soled shoe and the foot it encases – are raised when the fish is disturbed. The stonefish's survival depends largely on camouflage and immobility (both attributes contributing to its name) and it may not move away from an advancing human. Occasionally a stonefish spine won't have any venom associated with it. It's thought that this is because the venom is regenerated very slowly.

The well-camouflaged reef stonefish is the most venomous fish known. Its sting is extremely painful and has caused several fatalities.

Symptoms

The symptoms are similar to those described on page 126, but are often more severe. A sting from a stonefish may result in death.

CASE REPORT. Dr J.L.B. Smith (from the South African institute of ichthyology that bears his name), a world leader in marine biology, was collecting specimens when he was stung by a stonefish, two spines shallowly penetrating one of his fingers. Within five minutes the pain had spread from his finger to his hand, and was of an intensity he'd never before experienced.

"My wife injected me with novocaine and for a short time this had some effect, but the pain had become a searing agony, mostly across the back of the hand, with spasms reaching the head, neck and shoulder. The perspiration was such that my wife thought someone had splashed me with water. At about two-and-a-half-hours after the stab, my wife injected me with morphine. I felt drowsy, but the drug had no effect upon the pain.

"My wife decided to try hot-water immersion treatment. The effect was dramatic. The agony diminished rapidly to bearable proportions, and I returned to normal consciousness with an unquenchable thirst. We continued the treatment and I drank innumerable cups of tea for the next four hours, by which time the intense agony no longer recurred on removal of the wound from hot water. In the morning, the thumb was greatly enlarged, and had turned black all around the area of the stabs, and was without sensation. The hand was greatly swollen, as was the lower forearm, and was intensely painful to touch 24 hours after the stab."

The site became infected but was effectively treated with antibiotics. Months later the hand was still weak, slightly swollen, painful when used and the surrounding joints barely moveable. Dr Smith's general health was also impaired.

Prevention

Wear tough, thick-soled shoes when in danger areas. Be particularly careful on coral reefs and while entering or leaving boats. A stonefish sting is said by some fishermen to ensure some degree of immunity to further stings, although there is no scientific evidence to support this.

Scorpionfishes

Family: Scorpaenidae.
Dangerous species: *Apistus carinatus, Centropogon australis, Notesthes robusta, Scorpaena guttata, S. plumieri, Scorpaenopsis diabolus* and others.
Common names: Bullrout, devilfish, false stonefish, firefish, fortesque, goblinfish, kroki, jacopever, lionfish, redfish, red rock cod, rock cod, rockfish, roguefish, saddlehead, scorpion cod, sulky, waspfish.
Distribution: Widespread throughout tropical, subtropical and temperate regions. Some species even occur in the Antarctic.

This family has at least 330 members, including some of the world's most venomous fish. They are perch-like with large, scraggy heads and spines on their fins. Generally, their colouration matches that of their environment; in clear tropical waters with coral, the fishes tend to be colourful, sporting reds, blues and yellows, while in murky estuaries and harbours they are dull and brown. They vary in length from a few centimetres to a metre.

Butterfly cod

(*Pterois volitans, P. antennata, P. russeli, P. zebra* and others)
Also known as red fire fish, lionfish, zebrafish, coral cod, fire cod, turkeyfish and tigerfish, these attractive, brightly coloured fishes grow to 30 cm in length and are found in shallow water over coral reefs and around rocks. Large specimens are found in the tropics and subtropics, with juvenile specimens sometimes found in temperate regions. They frequently swim in pairs, show little fear and may orientate their body so that their 13 dorsal spines project forward. They also have anal and pelvic spines.

Devilfish

(*Inimicus barbatus, I. didactylus, I. japonicus*)
Also known as demon stinger and bearded ghoul, these rather grotesque fishes commonly grow to 30 cm in length and are usually found in deep water offshore, but occasionally inhabit rivers and estuaries. They've been known to attack underwater photographers and are a menace to trawler fishermen.

GERRY ALLEN

The spotfin lionfish, like other lionfishes, is a nocturnal bottom-dwelling species, feeding mostly on crustaceans. The dorsal spines are associated with venom glands, and stingings result in excruciating pain.

Red rock cod
(*Scorpaena cardinalis* and others)
Also known as red scorpion cod and mouth almighty, this fish grows to 35 cm in length, is coloured a deep sunset red, and resembles in form and colouring the rocks and weeds among which it lives. It normally possesses 12 dorsal spines. The grotesque head is associated with a funnel-like mouth, source of the name mouth almighty. There are many short, sharp, broad-based spines on the head.

A common species along the east coast, the red rock cod is often caught by fishermen. Care must be taken when removing it from the hook as it possesses numerous spines on the head and along the dorsal fin.

Stingrays

Families: Dasyatididae (sting or whipray, giant stingray), Gymnuridae (butterfly or rat-tailed ray), Myliobatidae (eagle or bat ray), Urolophidae (stingaree, round stingray), Rhinopteridae (cow-nose ray).
Distribution: Tropical to temperate waters.

These flattened relatives of the shark have one or more long, bony spines at the base of the tail, which they use for self defence. Although stingrays are said to be shallow-water creatures, I've often encountered large specimens (2 x 4 m) in the tropical Pacific at depths of 30–60 m and some may occur at oceanic depths of over 500 m. Many lose their long tails, probably to sharks. They often appear interested in divers and will sometimes swim with them; as long as you

KEVIN DEACON

The common stingaree, found off eastern Australia from Cape Howe in southern NSW to Caloundra in southern Queensland, may reach half a metre in length.

stay away from the vertebral column you shouldn't trigger a strike. Divers often feed rays and allow them to glide over them. They are very gentle, delicate animals, with behaviour sometimes reminiscent of a pet cat or dog.

Stingrays often lie submerged on the sea-floor, only a pair of eyes or a section of tail showing above an elevated disc of sand or mud until with a sudden swirl of detritus the ray elegantly glides away, sometimes very quickly.

They can be inadvertently stood upon, or otherwise disturbed, by an unsuspecting wader in which case the stingray defends itself by swinging its tail quickly over the top of its body, driving the spine into anything that happens to be above it, usually an ankle.

Symptoms

The spine may puncture the skin and inject venom. Its serrated edge can cause serious, potentially lethal lacerations. Parts of the spine, marine organisms and a toxic slime may be left in the wound, leading to infections and local inflammation. The local injury causes bleeding or death of tissue a few centimetres or more around the wound, and this condition and the resulting symptoms may take months to heal.

⊕ **For first aid see page 176.**

Prevention

● Footwear may not be adequate to protect the feet or lower legs from stingray injuries. Shuffling the feet while wading in areas frequented by stingrays will usually cause them to move away.

● Diving into shallow waters where these animals are seen should be avoided.

● Scuba divers should take care when settling on the seabed.

● Exercise care when handling fishing nets.

Catfishes

Families: Plotosidae and Ariidae.
Dangerous species: *Cnidoglanis* spp.,
Plotosus spp., *Tachysurus* spp.,
Netuma spp. and others.
Common names: Sea barbel, striped
catfish, eel-tailed catfish, cobbler, cattie.
Distribution: Tropical, subtropical
and temperate waters.

The name catfish comes from the harmless "whiskers" (sensory barbels) protruding from around the mouth, used by the fish to detect food under the sand. The fish are often encountered in mud flats, rivers, estuaries, lakes and on beaches, and are frequently trapped in fishing nets. Marine catfish vary in size from 5 cm to 1 m in length.

RON AND VALERIE TAYLOR/NATURE FOCUS

Juvenile striped catfish swim together in curious tight aggregations, balls of fish that are in constant motion as each outside fish endeavours to move into the centre, pushing other fish out.

Both fresh- and saltwater catfish are dangerous to handle. They have three barbed, serrated spines attached to the dorsal and two lateral (pectoral) fins, which usually have a skin-like covering. When contact is made between the spine and the victim's skin, the covering is pierced and the spine enters the victim. Venom then passes from a gland at the base of the spine, along it and into the wound. If the spine breaks off in the wound, removal will frequently cause further tissue damage, so it's often best to have it removed surgically.

The spines can cause injury even after the fish is dead.

Other venomous fishes

Old Wife

Family: Enoplosidae.

Dangerous species: *Enoplosus armatus*.

Common names: Zebrafish, bastard dory.

Rabbitfish

Family: Siganidae.

Dangerous species: *Siganus lineatus*, *S. rivulatus* and others.

Common names: Happy moments, golden-lines spinefoot, black trevally, mi mi, black spinefoot, spinefoot, stinging bream.

Surgeonfish and unicornfish

Family: Acanthuridae.

Dangerous species: *Acanthurus dussumieri*, *A. triostegus* and others, *Naso* spp.

Common names: Tang, doctorfish, spinetail.

Stargazer

Family: Uranoscopidae.

Dangerous species: *Uranoscopus duvali*, *Kathetostoma laeve*, *K. nigrofasciatum*, *Ichthyscopus barbatus*.

Common names: Deepwater or fringed stargazer, stonelifter.

Frogfish

Family: Batrachoididae.

Dangerous species: *Halophryne diemensis*, *Batrachoides cirrhosus*, *Opsanus tau* and others.

Common names: Toadfish, bastard stonefish, munda, sapo, oysterfish.

Distribution: Tropical, subtropical and temperate waters.

Sharp spines capable of causing a nasty laceration are present in the armouries of enough fish species to make it worthwhile to handle all fish with caution, whether they're known to be venomous or not. There's also

The old wife has a series of sharp spines along its dorsal fin that may be venomous. The name is said to be derived from the fish's habit of grinding its teeth to produce a "grumbling" sound.

uncertainty about which species have venom glands connected to their spines and which don't. It does seem, however, that the more an injury from a fish bleeds, the less severe the pain will be, perhaps due to what venom may be present being washed out by the blood.

The positions of the spines varies from species to species. The old wife, a 20–25 cm fish well known to divers because of its distinctive shape and zebra-like markings, has knife-like dorsal spines. Although they've been described as venomous, I find lacerations from the spines relatively painless. The fins of the rabbitfish bear numerous spines – 13 dorsal, four pelvic and seven anal – all with associated venom glands (the common name "happy moments" is an ironic tribute to the pain it can inflict). Surgeonfish and unicornfish, colourful reef dwellers, have blade-like spines at the base of the tail on each side of the body, often surrounded by bright warning colours. The spines may be venomous, although this hasn't been confirmed.

RON AND VALERIE TAYLOR

Surgeonfishes are named for the scalpel-shaped spines lying at the base of the tail. If this pencilled surgeonfish is harassed it can erect its spines and use them to slash its attacker with a rapid flick of the tail.

Injuries from these active swimmers will usually only occur when they've been caught by anglers or in nets. The other common injuries from fish spines occur when swimmers and reef-walkers step on bottom-dwelling fish, which are often well camouflaged and may bury themselves. One such species is the stargazer, a fish with a square head and a vertical mouth with fringed lips. The eyes are on the flat upper surface of the head, enabling the fish to spend a large part of its time buried in the mud with only the eyes and a portion of the mouth protruding. Its venom apparatus consists of two shoulder spines, one on either side, each of which protrudes through a sheath of skin. Glands deliver the venom along double grooves on each spine. Some stargazers are capable of inflicting an electric discharge similar to that of electric rays and eels.

Another bottom-dweller is the frogfish, a scaleless fish with frilly side-fins that grows to approximately 25 cm in length. Usually found among stones and coral and under rock ledges, they sometimes creep out over mudflats, able to survive long periods out of water. Their name refers to their habit of producing a loud frog-like croaking with their swim bladder. On their first dorsal fin and gill covers are spines with a hollow shaft through which venom is delivered.

Part   I V

OTHER VENOMOUS MARINE ANIMALS

Venom has evolved numerous times and in many different forms in marine creatures. Envenomation is a very efficient method of prey capture and can double as a defence. The species covered in this final marine section include some of the most venomous animals known to man, such as the blue-ringed octopus and sea-snakes. Sponges, one of the simplest multicellular animals, are also included because of the severe reactions that can be caused by the tiny skeletal elements called spicules that are embedded in their bodies and the toxic slime that some species produce.

None of the animals covered here are aggressive. In fact most of them must be harassed before they use their venoms. Sea-snakes often approach divers but this appears to be based on curiosity. The blue-ringed octopus has a fearsome reputation but it too will only bite when directly threatened. A little caution and common sense is probably all that's needed to avoid an unfortunate encounter with any of these animals.

Because of the diverse nature of the species covered here, the symptoms and treatment of their bites vary widely and the individual species accounts should be consulted for this information.

Blue-ringed octopus

Class: Cephalopoda.
Dangerous species: *Hapalochlaena maculosa*,
H. lunulata.
Common names: Common ringed,
blue-banded or spotted octopus.
Distribution: Indian and Pacific oceans;
all around Australia.

GERRY ALLEN

The blue-ringed octopus is often stranded in rockpools at low tide and its bright colours make it attractive to children, who should be warned of its dangers before they explore rock platforms.

This attractive little animal – even with tentacles extended, a blue-ringed octopus is smaller than an outstretched hand – is found in rock crevices both along the water's edge and in deeper water. It is also often stranded in rock pools after big tides.

The two species differ slightly in size but are essentially indistinguishable. They are both distinctively marked, yellowish with very dark bands containing blue or purple circles or lines. The stability of this pattern is unusual because the colours of other octopuses change according to their surroundings and moods. Inoffensive by nature, a blue-ringed octopus is usually relatively drab, blending perfectly with its surroundings. But if annoyed, its background colour will instantly darken and the blue rings brighten, becoming iridescent and possibly arousing the curiosity of a potential victim, especially a child.

The world's most lethal octopus, the blue-ringed has a bite that's small and relatively painless, but it injects venom through the beak, which is found at the base of the tentacles.

Symptoms

Handling this creature has resulted in death. The bite may go unnoticed by the victim until the effects of the venom are felt.

The injected venom can produce partial or total muscular paralysis within minutes, leading to cessation of breathing. Many such incidents have probably escaped detection by the coroner, as autopsy features are non-specific and the bite fades after the victim's death.

Vomiting sometimes occurs and the victim may remain fully conscious but unable to talk due to the paralysis. Death is due to respiratory failure, but can be prevented by adequate first aid. Health-care professionals need to be aware that the victim, even though completely paralysed, is totally conscious of his or her surroundings.

CASE REPORT. A diver found a small, attractive octopus with iridescent blue rings hiding in a shell. She placed it under her wetsuit vest, intending to show it to her companion. After the dive she complained of double vision and breathing difficulties. Fortunately, her companion recognised the octopus and the symptoms and kept her alive by mouth-to-mouth resuscitation until they reached the hospital.

The victim later pointed out that she wasn't encouraged by comments such as "it looks as though she isn't going to make it" from paramedics, who hadn't realised that she was fully conscious in spite of being paralysed.

⊕ **For first aid see page 176.**

Prevention

● Avoid contact with the octopus and treat apparently empty shells with caution.
● The public should be educated on the dangers of this animal. This is especially true of children, who may be attracted by its bright colours.

Cone shells

Family: Conidae.

Dangerous species: *Conus catus* (cat cone), *C. geographus* (geographer cone), *C. striatus* (striated cone), *C. tulipa* (tulip cone), *C. magus* (magician's cone, cone of maggii), *C. marmoreus* (marbled cone), *C. omaria* (pearled cone), *C. textile* (cloth of gold, textile cone, woven cone).

Distribution: Many of the dangerous species occur in the Indian and Pacific oceans.

Less than 10 of the more than 600 members of the cone shell family are reported to deliver a lethal sting to humans. The venom, which causes death in 25 per cent of cases, is injected into prey using a tiny dart shot from a tubular appendage (the proboscis) that the creature can direct to any part of its shell – so there is no "safe" way to hold a live cone shell. The primary use of the venom is to immobilise prey (usually small fish), but the mollusc will use the proboscis as a weapon when annoyed or disturbed, such as when it's handled. Expert knowledge is required to differentiate venomous from harmless cone shells, and it is advisable to avoid handling them at all.

Symptoms

The initial sting is only painful in some cases. The toxin can affect the heart, skeletal and respiratory muscles, causing muscle spasms and paralysis. Death is usually from respiratory failure.

⊕ **For first aid see page 177.**

Prevention

- Avoid picking up live cone shells as there isn't anywhere that they can be safely held. If you must collect them, use long tongs and a tough receptacle and only handle the live cone shells with thick gloves.
- Do not place live cone shells in your pockets. The poisonous dart can penetrate clothing.
- Educate people at risk – shell collectors, reef visitors and schoolchildren, for example. Many stings occur when collectors are cleaning the shells.

A nasty surprise is in store for unwary shell collectors who pick up a live cloth of gold (above) or marbled cone shell (below) – both are capable of inflicting a deadly sting with their extendable proboscis. Cone shells are mostly nocturnal, hiding beneath the sand or coral rubble during the day and emerging at night to hunt their prey, which may include other molluscs or small fish.

Sea-snakes

Family: Elapidae; subfamily Hydrophiinae.

Dangerous species: *Aipysurus* spp.,
Astrotia stokesii, Enhydrina schistosa
(beaked sea-snake), *Hydrophis* spp.,
Lapemis hardwickii, Laticauda spp.
(banded sea-snakes), *Pelamis platurus*
(yellow-bellied sea-snake), and others.

Distribution: Tropical and subtropical
waters of the Indian and Pacific oceans.

There are currently around 50 known species of these air-breathing reptiles. Although few are dangerous to humans, all have venom glands and fangs for capturing their prey. They are divided into two families, the Hydrophiidae, all species of which live all of their lives at sea, and the Laticaudidae, whose members are partly terrestrial and lay their eggs along the shoreline. The feature that distinguishes sea-snakes from land snakes (which may also swim) is their paddle-shaped tail.

In certain areas sea-snakes will approach divers underwater. These advances are probably inspired by curiosity and it's rare for sea-snakes to bite without provocation. Most bites occur when a snake is caught in fishing nets or handled.

Sea-snakes have extremely potent venom – the world's most potent snake venom is that of the hook-nosed or beaked sea-snake, *Enhydrina schistosa*. However, their fangs are relatively short, so the delivery of venom to humans is quite inefficient. Sea-snake folklore suggests that these snakes can only bite a person between the fingers but the gape of a sea-snake equals that of a land snake and, regardless of head size, they can bite a person anywhere. Like other snakes, sea-snakes can choose how much venom to inject when they bite and in many cases won't inject any at all, a so-called "dry bite".

Symptoms

Bites occasionally result in severe lacerations and blood loss, with symptoms becoming evident within 30–120 minutes. Muscle weakness may develop into paralysis, including respiratory-muscle paralysis and asphyxia (lack of oxygen), and finally heart failure.

KEVIN DEACON

The most common sea-snake in Australia's coral reefs, the olive sea-snake often approaches divers. These inspections appear to be driven by curiosity rather than aggression and bites are extremely rare.

Weakness of the eyelids, often one of the earliest signs, is characteristic and may persist for days. Muscular twitchings, writhings and spasms, difficulty with speech and swallowing, and facial and eye paralysis (causing double or blurred vision) may also occur.

Early deaths are usually due to respiratory failure, while cardiac effects and renal failure are the usual causes of death in delayed cases.

➕ For first aid see page 177.

Prevention
- Don't handle sea-snakes.
- Shuffle feet when walking on a muddy bottom.
- Wear protective clothing while underwater.

CASE REPORT. In October 1979, a two-year-old girl began screaming while playing in the water at a Queensland beach. Her mother noticed a snake wrapped around her daughter's left ankle before it swam off.

The mother used her hands as a tourniquet around the child's calf, and both were rushed to an ambulance station. After the ambulance officer had cleaned the wound, the mother released her grip on the child's leg and within 30 seconds she became drowsy and developed droopy eyelids. En route to hospital, she started to vomit and respiratory distress became obvious.

On arrival at hospital, 20 minutes after envenomation (four minutes after the onset of symptoms), the child was unconscious, cyanosed (turning blue from lack of oxygen) and had tonic (tense) movements of the limbs. Her breathing deteriorated and, approximately 40 minutes after envenomation, she required resuscitation and sea-snake antivenom.

The following day she slept most of the time but seemed to hallucinate occasionally. At the end of the second day, she was still unstable but able to stand with support. By the fifth day, the child's condition was much improved and one month after the incident she was functioning normally, except for some return of unstable gait when she was tired.

Sea urchins

Family: Diadematidae.

Dangerous species: *Centrostephanus rodgersi, C. tenuispinus, Diadema setosum* (long-spined or black sea urchin), *D. savignyi* (needle-spine urchin), *Echinothrix calamaris, E. diadema*.

Family: Echinothuridae.

Dangerous species: *Araeosoma thetidis, Asthenosoma varium, A. ijimai* (tam o'shanter urchins).

Family: Temnopleuridae.

Dangerous species: *Salmacis sphaeroides*.

Family: Toxopneustidae (flower urchin).

Dangerous species: *Toxopneustes pileolus, Tripneustes gratilla*.

Distribution: Found in all oceans, the venomous urchins occur in the tropics, subtropics and some extend to temperate waters.

KEVIN DEACON

The flower-like appendages on this flower urchin, called pedicellariae, are used to keep debris and enemies at bay. Each pedicellarium has a venom gland, the product of which can be lethal.

Sea urchins belong to the phylum Echinodermata, named after the hedgehog (*Echinos*) because of their many-spined appearance. They are slow-moving grazers that come in a wide variety of colours, shapes and sizes. Their spines may be short and fat or long and needle-like and of the 600 known species, approximately 80 are thought to be venomous or poisonous to humans. In some, such as the long-spined sea urchin, the damage is done mainly by sharp, brittle spines that penetrate the victim's skin and break off. The spines of *Diadema* will disappear within a few days, but the venomous spines of *Echinothrix* may remain in the skin for many months, or may eventually emerge at sites distant from the original wound. The spines are covered by a black pigment, which can be mistaken for the actual spine during its removal. *Asthenosoma* spines are enclosed in venom glands.

Along with their spines, many echinoderms have tiny, snapping pincer-like organs called pedicellariae scattered over their surface. Often attached to a short stalk, they are used to keep enemies and possibly debris off the animal, and in some species have powerful venom associated with them. The most venomous sea urchins are the flower urchins, which have short spines almost concealed by the array of flower-like pedicellariae. Deaths from the paralysing venom of the pedicellariae have been reported.

The crown-of-thorns starfish, *Acanthaster planci*, also an echinoderm, can cause damage by piercing the skin with its spines, and introducing torn tissue into the wound. This seems to cause a far more inflammatory action than that of the urchins and commonly causes nausea and/or vomiting, suggesting the presence of a venom. Injuries have become more frequent since divers began trying to eradicate the crown-of-thorns from reefs.

In recent years, outbreaks of crown-of-thorns starfish have caused considerable damage to the GBR. The starfish feed on coral polyps and it's claimed that an infestation can destroy reefs at a rate of 5 km per month.

TONY KARACSONYI

CASE REPORT. A 40-year-old diver rested his thigh on a crown-of-thorns while taking photographs on the GBR when he suddenly felt a severe pain. He thought he was going to lose consciousness, but managed to reach the surface with the crown-of-thorns still attached to his leg. At that stage, he was still able to use the affected limb but was in extreme pain, which increased over the next few minutes. Eventually, he lost mobility in the leg.

Although extremely painful, it was easy to pull out many of the exposed spines, but there were others that couldn't be removed. There was a complete numbness below the injury, without any sensation of touch or deep pressure. Swelling developed rapidly and vomiting developed about half an hour after the injury, continuing for some hours. The patient developed painful joints for three days, headaches for two days and was still retching and feeling nauseated five days after the injury. He also coughed salty mucus, felt very giddy and developed a fever ("cold sweats"). He has no memory of the trip to hospital where he was treated for pain and vomiting and given a tetanus injection. He was then flown to Sydney in a delirious state.

On examination, the thigh was very swollen and the pain restricted movement. Multiple wounds showed where the spines had penetrated the skin and their precise locations were identified with ultrasound. Under general anaesthesia nine remaining spines were removed, antibiotic ointment was applied and the wounds closed. Immediately after the spines were removed, the patient's general symptoms ceased. The retching and nausea cleared up and the pain and discomfort were greatly reduced.

➕ **For first aid see page 178.**

Prevention
- Stay away from these creatures.
- Wear protective, hard-soled shoes when walking on reefs.
- Although some spines will easily penetrate gloves, these are still of some protective value.

Sponges

Phylum: Porifera.

Dangerous species: *Biemna saucia, Neofibularia irata, N. mordens, Lissodendoryx* spp.

Distribution: All waters, from the tropics to the polar regions. Toxic species are found mainly in temperate and tropical waters.

Sponges are sedentary animals that live attached to the sea-floor, filtering food particles from the surrounding water. Many have a fibrous skeleton formed of a keratin-like substance called spongin, which is found only in sponges. It's very difficult to identify different species of sponge as colour and growth form can vary greatly within a single species. The features used to distinguish the species are the shapes of tiny skeletal elements called spicules embedded in the body of the sponge. The spicules may be made of calcium carbonate or silica and are responsible for many of the injuries associated with contact with sponges. About a dozen of the 5000 or so known species also possess poorly understood toxins. Being attached to the sea floor and hence unable to escape from predators, some sponges have developed toxins and distasteful compounds. *Neofibularia irata*, a sponge found on the GBR, produces copious quantities of mucus that contains an irritating toxin.

Symptoms

A contact dermatitis develops at the area of sponge contact. Irritation is felt after 5–120 minutes, brought on by wetting or rubbing the area. The dermatitis may progress over the next day or so and the victim feels as if ground glass has been rubbed into the skin. Abnormal sensations may also be felt and inflammatory and painful reactions around the area can persist for a week or more. Some patients may be incapacitated by the symptoms without showing any obvious manifestations.

Thick-skinned areas show less response, but experience the same degree of pain. The palms of the hands and fingers may show little more than a reddish, blotchy effect to explain the severe symptoms. Occasionally a dermatological disease, cheiropompholyx, will develop following exposure to a sponge. The

The sponge *Neofibularia irata* forms encrusting mats, growing over corals and other organisms. Sponges are thought to be among the most primitive multi-celled animals. They come in a bewildering array of colours and shapes, making them very difficult to identify.

skin may peel or flake off in the second or third week, giving the appearance of peeling sunburn. Skin wounds have developed from sponges that have been deep frozen or dried for many years.

➕ **For first aid see page 178.**

Ringed or segmented worms

Family: Amphinomidae.
Dangerous species: *Chloeia flava* (beautiful seamouse, bristle worm), *Eurythoe complanata* (bristle worm).
Family: Eunicidae.
Dangerous species: *Eunice aphroditois* (biting reef worm)
Family: Aphroditidae.
Dangerous species: *Aphrodita australis* (seamouse).
Distribution: Tropical, subtropical and temperate waters; most of the dangerous species are tropical.

The bodies of these animals are segmented, each segment with paddle-like limbs bearing bundles of fine bristles. They often lie under rocks or in corals and come in a variety of colours, sometimes very attractively marked. They cause injury either by penetration of the bristles or by biting. The bristles of the bristleworms (Amphinomidae) are composed of calcium carbonate, which explains their irritant effect but not the generalised symptoms that have been reported.

The biting reef worm may grow to 1.5 m in length and so can inflict quite severe biting wounds. The bristle worm may be a nuisance to fishermen when catching certain fish that feed with them.

Symptoms

Contact with bristle worms may produce an intense itching or burning sensation lasting up to a week, and blisters filled with clear fluid or blood may develop. The surrounding tissues may become painful and swollen, the joints may become stiff or immobile and lymph glands may swell and become tender. The overall reaction lasts for 7–10 days, but is worse in the first to third days, while secondary infection may produce a recurrence of symptoms days later. Numbness over the area may persist for several weeks.

Severe general reactions have been reported, at least with the bristle worm. These are cardiovascular: an increased pulse rate with palpitations, fainting and chest pain. The patient feels very ill and may be compelled to rest for a

KAREN GOWLETT-HOLMES

Care should be taken when fossicking around at low tide on rocky shores –
the white-collared sea worm lives under rocks at the low-tide level and can deliver
a nasty bite.

day or more. The importance of allergic factors is unknown.

Bites from segmented worms are a few millimetres in diameter and rapidly
become hot, swollen and inflamed and may remain so for a day or longer.

⊕ **For first aid see page 178.**

Prevention

- Avoid contact with these worms.
- Be wary when turning over rocks and corals.
- Wear protective clothing and gloves (although these may not always
  suffice).
- Be especially wary when handling the Barrier Reef yellow sweetlip,
  or other fish that coexist with these worms.

FIRST AID AND MEDICAL TREATMENT

Although it's something that no-one wishes to contemplate, there's always a possibility that one day you'll have to come to the aid of a seriously injured person. For this reason, it's important to know and understand basic first aid. It's easy to learn and it may one day help you to save someone's life.

Everyone should make themselves familiar with the information contained in Parts I and II of this chapter. Part I contains general first-aid advice, information on first-aid kits and emergency contact numbers. Part II contains detailed information for the treatment of the various bites and stings described earlier. Part III of this chapter covers some of the medical aspects of first aid. The information in this section is detailed and quite complicated as it's aimed mainly at health professionals.

The information in Part I was largely obtained from St John Ambulance's AUSTRALIAN FIRST AID *manual, reproduced by kind permission of St John Ambulance Australia, with additional material on cardiopulmonary resuscitation, expired air resuscitation and allergic reactions from Dr Carl Edmonds.*

The information contained in this chapter is not a substitute for supervised practical first-aid training from a qualified instructor. For details of training courses ring St John Ambulance from anywhere in Australia on 1300 360 455.

Many of Australia's dangerous creatures have adapted to life in an urban environment (opposite) so it's important to know the necessary first aid.

GENERAL FIRST-AID ADVICE
THE DRABC ACTION PLAN

St John Ambulance Australia has developed the DRABC action plan for response in an accident or emergency. DRABC stands for:

DANGER

RESPONSE

AIRWAY

BREATHING

CIRCULATION

D Check for DANGER

– to you
– to others
– to the casualty

● Make sure that no-one else gets hurt – you won't be able to help if you are also a casualty.

● Only proceed if it's safe to do so.

R Check RESPONSE

– is the casualty conscious?

● Gently shake the casualty and ask: "Can you hear me?", "What is your name?"

● If the casualty is conscious, check for and manage bleeding and other injuries (see below).

● If the casualty is unconscious they should be turned on their side.

A Clear and open the AIRWAY

Clearing the airway:

1. With the patient supported on the side, tilt the head backwards and slightly down.

2. Open the mouth and clear any foreign objects. Only remove dentures

if loose or broken.

Opening the airway:

1. Place one hand high on the patient's forehead.
2. Support the chin with the other hand.
3. Gently lift the head backwards.
4. Lift the jaw forward and open the patient's mouth slightly.

B Check for BREATHING

- look for chest movements
- place your head close to the patient's mouth and listen for the sound of breathing
- feel for expired air on your cheek
- look, listen and feel for up to 10 seconds before deciding that breathing is absent
- If the patient is breathing, ensure that they are in a stable side position. Check for and manage bleeding and other injuries.
- If the casualty isn't breathing, turn onto back and commence expired air resuscitation (EAR – see below), giving at least two effective rescue breaths, each of which makes the chest rise and fall.

C Check for CIRCULATION

- Check the carotid pulse by feeling with the ends of your fingers in the groove on either side of the windpipe (neck) for up to 10 seconds, during which look for any other signs of circulation such as movement, including swallowing or breathing, and return of colour to the face.
- If pulse is present, continue EAR at the rate of 15 breaths per minute. Check breathing and pulse about every minute.
- If pulse isn't present or there are no other signs of circulation, commence cardiopulmonary resuscitation (CPR – see below) immediately.
- Check breathing and pulse after one minute, then about every minute. If the pulse returns, continue EAR. If breathing returns, turn the patient to a stable side position. Check for and manage shock, bleeding and other injuries.
- Seek medical aid.

BASIC CARDIOPULMONARY RESUSCITATION
(CPR)
AND EXPIRED AIR RESUSCITATION
(EAR)

by Dr Carl Edmonds

Basic life support prevents death by supporting the respiratory and cardiac systems when they cease to function. The objective is to provide oxygen to the brain, heart and other vital organs until appropriate medical treatment (advanced life support) can replace or restore normal respiratory and cardiovascular function.

When breathing ceases (primary respiratory arrest) the heart can continue to pump blood for several minutes and the oxygen in the lungs and blood will still circulate to the brain and other organs. Respiratory arrest can be due to problems within the lungs, in the muscles needed for breathing, in the nerve supply to these muscles, or in the part of the brain that controls breathing. It may result from drowning, envenomation or poisoning and is treated by artificial respiration, usually EAR, otherwise known as mouth-to-mouth resuscitation.

When the heart stops beating (primary cardiac arrest) oxygen ceases to be circulated by the blood and the oxygen stored in the vital organs is depleted within a few seconds. Cardiac arrest can be due to disruption of the cardiac muscle contraction, the rhythm of heart contraction, the nerve supply, or the areas of the brain that control heart activity. It may result from lack of oxygen (with respiratory arrest), envenomation or poisoning. It's initially treated by external cardiac compression ("heart massage").

THE ABC OF BASIC EAR AND CPR

A is for airway

An effective airway must be established as soon as possible – no time should be lost.

1. Quickly examine the patient's mouth and throat, cleaning them out with fingers or a cloth.
2. Roll the patient onto his/her back and tilt the head backwards.
3. Lift the jaw forward, bringing the lower teeth in line with the upper teeth. This will pull the relaxed tongue away from the back of the throat. Sometimes a pad of clothing or a sand mound under the patient's shoulders will help.

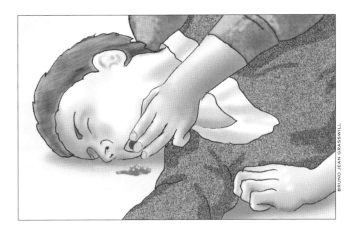

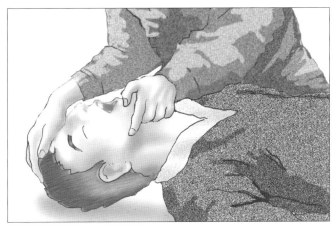

B is for breathing

1. Kneel beside the patient's head.

2. With one hand block off the nostrils. With the other hand, cradle the jaw to maintain a backward tilt of the head.

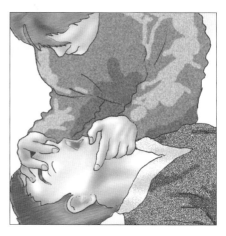

3. Inhale and fit your lips around the patient's mouth to make an airtight seal, then breathe into the patient. If the patient is an adult, breathe fully; for a child shallower and gentler. At the same time look to see if the patient's chest rises. If it doesn't, the airway isn't completely clear.

4. Remove your lips from the patient and allow him/her to exhale (this will happen without assistance). Check that the chest falls as the patient exhales.

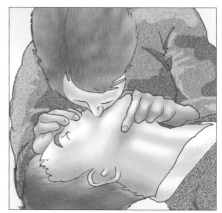

5. Repeat this cycle, fully inflating the patient's chest.

6. Check for a carotid pulse by feeling with the ends of your fingers in the groove on either side of the windpipe (neck). If there is no pulse, CPR must be performed (see section C).

7. If there is a pulse but the patient is still not breathing, continue to give breaths at a rate of one every four seconds for adults or one every three seconds for children. Check for a pulse about once a minute.

Because of the remote possibility that infection will be transmitted between patient and rescuer, use an artificial airway, if one is available, to ventilate the victim. These are mechanical devices – masks or tubes – that prevent direct contact between rescuer and patient and improve the efficiency of artificial respiration. Apart from reducing the risk of disease transmission, these devices have the advantage of holding the patient's tongue away from the airway.

C is for circulation

If the heart has stopped beating there won't be a pulse at the wrist, over the heart or on the carotid arteries. The patient will have enlarged pupils that don't react to light, and there'll be no improvement in colour (the patient will be bluish), even after the commencement of artificial respiration. In these circumstances external cardiac massage must commence immediately, in conjunction with mouth-to-mouth resuscitation.

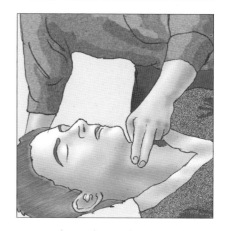

1. Place the patient on his/her back on a hard surface – not a bed or couch.
2. Take up a position at the right side of the patient's chest and place the heel of your left hand on the lower half of the breastbone (sternum) with the middle finger across the chest in line with the nipples. In this position a ridge across the lower third of the breastbone will fit into the groove between the base of the thumb and the base of the hand.

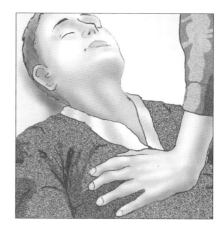

3. Place your right hand on the left and, keeping your arms straight with your shoulders directly above the patient, use your own weight to depress the patient's breastbone by 4–5 cm. For a child, use only one hand and depress 2–3 cm; in the case of an infant use two fingers and depress 1–2 cm. Use a slow rhythmic motion producing 80–100 compressions per minute.

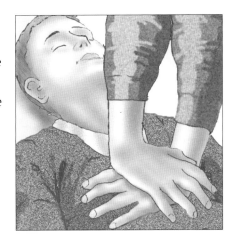

4. Expired air resuscitation and external cardiac compression may be carried out by two rescuers: a ratio of five compressions to one breath at 12 cycles per minute; or by one rescuer: a ratio of two breaths to 15 compressions at four cycles per minute.

Positioning the patient

For basic CPR to be effective, the patient must be lying on his/her back on a firm, flat surface. Even when performed correctly, external cardiac compression will produce inadequate blood flow to the brain if the head is positioned higher than the chest.

Moving the patient

The patient shouldn't be moved until effective CPR has been started and the patient has a pulse, or unless CPR can be performed without interruption during transit.

When to stop CPR

In cases of drowning or hypothermia (excessively low body temperature), spectacular successes have been achieved long after CPR would, under other circumstances, have been considered ineffectual. So resuscitation should be more aggressive and sustained in these cases. The other complication of hypothermia is that excessive manipulation and movement are likely to cause cardiac arrest. It is therefore important to ensure that breathing and pulse are absent before commencing resuscitation. Nevertheless, if the need for urgent CPR is apparent, it should not be withheld.

In some cases of envenomation there is a slight cardiac/respiratory activity that may not be obvious to observers. In these circumstances good results can still be obtained long after the patient appears to be dead or incapacitated, so CPR should be persevered with.　　　　　　　　　　　　　　　　　　CE

MANAGING BLOOD LOSS

Bites from creatures such as sharks and crocodiles can be severe and the most important first aid involves stopping blood loss. First-aid procedures for the management of blood loss are described below. Patients who experience major blood loss may also go into shock, the treatment of which is also outlined below.

External bleeding
1. Apply direct pressure to the wound with your fingers or hand. Encourage the casualty to do this (where practical).
2. As soon as possible, place a clean dressing over the wound. Apply a bulky pad extending beyond the edges of the wound and firmly bandage. If bleeding continues, leave the dressing in place and relocate the pad.
3. Do not disturb pads or bandages once bleeding is controlled.

Uncontrolled bleeding
If severe bleeding can't be controlled by direct pressure, it may be necessary to apply pressure to a pressure point above the wound. These are found on the main arteries (see diagram over). When bleeding has been controlled, remove pressure on the point and reapply direct pressure to the wound.

Occasionally, in major limb injuries such as partial amputations and shark attack, severe bleeding can't be controlled by direct pressure. Only then, it may be necessary to apply a constrictive bandage or tourniquet above the elbow or knee.

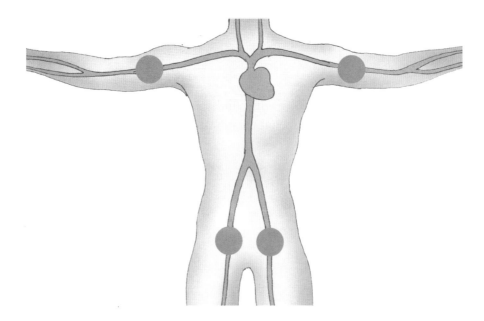

Using a constrictive bandage

1. Select a strip of firm cloth, at least 7.5 cm wide and about 75 cm long. This may be improvised from clothing.

2. Bind the cloth strip firmly around the injured limb above the bleeding point until a pulse can no longer be felt below the constrictive bandage and bleeding is controlled. Tie firmly.

3. Note the time of application. After 30 minutes, release the bandage and check for bleeding. If there is no bleeding remove it. If bleeding recommences, apply direct pressure. If this is unsuccessful, reapply the constrictive bandage and recheck every 30 minutes.

4. Ensure the bandage is clearly visible and inform medical aid of the location and time of its application.

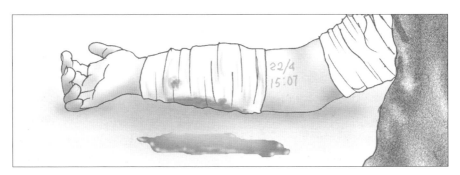

FIRST AID FOR ALLERGY AND ANAPHYLAXIS

By Dr Carl Edmonds

The bites and stings of some animals can produce an allergic reaction in people sensitive to them. If a person is especially sensitive, the reaction, called anaphylaxis, is potentially fatal and requires rapid first aid and medical treatment. For more detailed information on allergy/anaphylaxis see page 183.

1. In serious cases seek urgent medical advice.
2. Lay the patient down and give reassurance.
3. Give resuscitation when needed (page 159).
4. Stop administration of, or exposure to, the substance that caused the reaction.
5. Use soothing lotions such as calamine lotion on skin lesions.
6. Some medications used for asthma or hives may be employed, if skilled medical attention is unavailable (page 185).
7. Adrenaline is usually used in the medical treatment of severe allergy and anaphylaxis. One source of adrenaline that non-medicos can obtain is Eppy, an old-fashioned adrenaline spray used frequently for asthmatics in the past, but not very popular nowadays. It can be used as a "puffer" to allow the victim to inhale adrenaline into his/her lungs, where it's absorbed into the bloodstream. It's often been used to treat anaphylactic reaction, especially in very remote areas of the Pacific Islands.

FIRST-AID KITS

Every household should have at least one first-aid kit and preferably more – another in the car and one more to be used when camping away from the vehicle or bushwalking. A basic first-aid kit should contain items such as bandages, dressings, slings, scissors and safety pins. The contents should be periodically checked and shortages and expired-date items replaced.

Comprehensive first-aid kits are available from St John Ambulance Australia, the Australian Red Cross and Australian Geographic stores. A typical first-aid kit will usually contain:

a range of dressings and wound covers,

slings,

an emergency shock blanket,

sterile gloves,

a notepad and pencils,

resealable plastic bags,

disposable towels,

pads for bleeding control,

gauze swabs,

forceps,

safety pins,

scissors,

a first-aid book,

alcohol wipes for hand cleaning,

saline for eye/wound irrigation and wound cleaning and

Stingose spray for soothing bites and stings.

EMERGENCY NUMBERS FOR ADVICE ON BITES AND STINGS

Ambulance **000**

Poisons Information centres (Australia-wide) **13 11 26**

Commonwealth Serum Laboratories Limited (all-hours phone number for referral to a CSL consultant on the use of antivenom and the management of envenomation) **(03) 9389 1911**

Marine Stinger Advice Phone (for urgent medical advice for any serious marine envenomation) **(08) 8222 5116**

FIRST AID
FOR BITES AND STINGS

This section contains detailed information for first-aid treatment of the bites and stings mentioned in the various species accounts. To this information can be added some more general advice for what to do in the event of a serious bite or sting.

Some bites or stings are potentially fatal and anyone with such an injury requires urgent first aid, followed as soon as possible by emergency medical treatment. It's also important to seek medical assistance even if the victim appears to recover, especially in the event of weakness or problems with walking or coordination. For potentially fatal envenomation, first-aid measures shouldn't be discontinued to inspect the wound – especially if adequate treatment and antivenom aren't immediately available.

It's important not to give the patient alcohol or food, but simple clear fluids may be given if s/he is fully conscious. In assessing the patient, symptoms such as weakness, speech difficulties and drooping eyelids may indicate paralysis. In the event of a bite or sting, bring the culprit to the hospital with the patient – but only if it's possible to do so without placing yourself or others at risk.

If symptoms recur, the patient should receive expert medical attention. The recurrence of local signs of inflammation, some hours or days after the initial injury, may suggest either secondary infection or a foreign body reaction, both of which require medical attention. A tetanus booster may be required in some cases of spider, insect or snake bite, but this decision should be left to the treating doctor.

SNAKEBITE
by Dr Julian White

The local effects of snakebite

People often assume that if a snakebite is going to be significant, the location of the bite will be obvious and painful. Although some bites from snakes routinely cause local pain, and can cause quite extensive swelling, this isn't always the case. A brown-snake bite site in particular may be very hard to see, painless and easily missed.

Once venom is injected it spreads throughout the body. Perhaps because many of the more toxic venom components are relatively large molecules, they don't enter the bloodstream at the bite site, but travel through the lymph channels, passing through the lymph nodes in the groin (for bites on the leg) or armpit (for those on the arm). In the process they may cause pain or swelling of these nodes. The lymphatic system eventually dumps its contents into the bloodstream in the chest.

Once in the blood, venom can travel very quickly throughout the whole body, rapidly taking effect. The victim may experience a variety of fairly general symptoms and effects such as headache, nausea, vomiting, abdominal pain, dizziness, blurred vision and even collapse in some cases. In children in particular, severe bites can result in fits. This can be problematic because a child may be unable to tell anyone that s/he has been bitten by a snake, and finding a snakebite among the scrapes and scratches that most children get while playing may be impossible. Then, too, there are many reasons why a child may have fits, so snakebite may not be an obvious diagnosis.

The various toxins in snake venom have quite specific effects, and the pattern of these effects will depend on the species of snake. In the absence of a positive identification, this pattern may help doctors decide what type of snake was responsible for a bite, enabling them to choose the best antivenom. Snake-venom detection kits also aid the process of antivenom choice.

Snakebite paralysis caused by neurotoxins will take at least an hour to show effects and it is often several hours before these effects become severe. Often the first area to be paralysed is around the eye, with the upper eyelid becoming weak and drooping down. Victims describe the symptom, which doctors call "ptosis", as heavy or sleepy eyelids. Soon after, the patient's sight may become blurred or s/he may even experience double vision, followed by weakness of the tongue and voice. This then progresses to difficulty in swallowing and talking, and then general weakness in the arms and legs, making standing or walking difficult. Breathing is usually the last thing affected.

Muscle damage caused by myotoxins is often subtle at first. As the damage becomes severe, the victim will experience weakness and painful muscles, the pain made worse by movement. The urine will change colour, turning red or brown, before slowing or stopping if the kidneys are damaged, such damage usually only apparent to the victim when urine production decreases or ceases altogether.

If there are procoagulants in the venom, the victim may experience persistent bleeding from the bite, as well as any recent wound, and sometimes from the gums. Anticoagulant venoms may also cause persistent bleeding from the bite site.

Treatment of snakebite

First aid

Correct first aid can make the difference between surviving or dying from snakebite and its importance can't be overemphasised. It was known for many years that snake venoms moved through the lymph channels and that by splinting the bitten limb, the spread of venom could be greatly delayed. In 1978 this was developed, after a series of experiments on animals, into the current "pressure-immobilisation method" pioneered by Dr Struan Sutherland and his team, based at CSL and the Royal Children's Hospital, Melbourne.

The method is simple, superior to all others, and has proved effective in numerous cases of snakebite.

1. Move away from the snake if it's still present. **Do not** attempt to kill it, as this will waste time and increase the risk of further bites.
2. Don't panic; keep the victim lying down and as still as possible.
3. Don't clean or wash the bite area – doing so will interfere with venom detection at the hospital and thus impair treatment.
4. Firmly apply a broad bandage – the elastic type is ideal – to the bitten area, about as firmly as you would for a sprain. It shouldn't be so tight as to act as a tourniquet or cut off circulation. If a bandage isn't available, use strips of clothing or pantyhose. Be careful to move the

bitten limb as little as possible during bandaging and splinting.

5. Once the bite area is bandaged, extend the bandage to cover as much of the bitten limb as possible. Cut clothing away or bind over the top rather than increasing movement by attempting to remove it.

6. Fully immobilise the bitten limb using a splint and further bandaging. This immobilisation is a vital part of the treatment.

7. If the victim is semiconscious or vomiting, gently roll him/her onto their side to prevent inhalation of vomit or saliva.

8. Urgently seek medical attention.

9. Avoid giving any food or drink to the patient unless a long time will elapse before reaching medical aid, in which case offer water only, providing the patient is conscious and can swallow without difficulty.

10. Try to bring transport to the site and don't allow the patient to move independently as any movement will speed the effects of the venom.

To this list could be added a few extra points:

● If the snake has been killed, bring it to the hospital, but be very careful when handling it, especially around the head, to avoid accidental contact with the fangs.

● When assisting a snakebite victim, try to note when symptoms occur.

● If bitten when alone, try to leave a message so that your rescuers will have some idea what has happened and carry another in case you collapse before you are found. Note when the bite occurred, how many times you were bitten, and a description of the size and approximate colour of the snake.

● If you bind the limb, indicate the bite site on the outside of the bandage so that it can be located and swabbed for venom detection without removing the bandage.

Some things you shouldn't do:

Do not use a tourniquet.

Do not cut or suck the wound or apply any chemicals to it.

Do not wash or clean the wound.

Do not give any medications or alcohol.

Do not apply electric shock to the wound.

Do not let the victim walk around or be otherwise physically active.

Hospital treatment

Hospital treatment of snakebite can be summarised as follows:

- Recognising that a snakebite has occurred. This may sound obvious, but all too often victims don't know or can't say that they've been bitten.
- Setting up the initial management process. This usually means administering an intravenous drip, taking blood for testing, performing venom detection on the bite site or urine, careful examination for paralysis, myolysis (muscle destruction) and bleeding, and securing a supply of antivenom.
- Giving an initial dose of the appropriate antivenom as soon as it's indicated. It's best to use an antivenom specific for the type of snake involved, hence the value of venom detection, but if this isn't known there is a polyvalent antivenom that covers all types of snakes. It's more expensive and has a higher incidence of side effects, so it's only used in these cases.
- Repeating tests and examination as necessary and giving more antivenom if needed.
- All suspected snakebite victims are usually kept in hospital overnight, even if they seem well, as delayed effects occasionally occur.

Antivenom

Antivenom is a proven lifesaver but it can have side effects, so it should only be used by doctors, preferably in a hospital, and only if the patient has significant effects from the bite. Most snakebite victims experience only minor or no effects and won't need antivenom.

Antivenom is made by injecting animals (currently horses) with modified venom that prompts them to produce antibodies against the venom without harming them. Over time the amount of venom injected is increased, thereby increasing the number of antibodies produced. Eventually the animal is making large quantities of antibodies and becomes a regular blood donor. The blood is refined to produce a concentrated serum containing only the antibody, which forms the active part of the antivenom and destroys the venom when injected into a patient. It's a laborious process and it isn't surprising that antivenom can be quite expensive.

As Australian snake antivenoms are currently made from horse antibodies, people who are allergic to horses may react badly to them. Doctors therefore need to know of any allergies so that any reaction to the antivenom can be treated. But don't believe stories that antivenoms are worse than snakebites because they are simply untrue.

New methods of antivenom production currently being developed should make them safer and more effective. Australia is playing a prominent role in this process. JW

SPIDERS, INSECTS AND OTHER INVERTEBRATES

Funnel-web spiders

Funnel-web spider bites may cause the production of excess saliva or tears. Muscle twitching and goose bumps also occur in many cases of funnel-web spider envenomation. First aid for bites from any of the species of funnel-web spider is as for snakebite (page 168). There is an antivenom available for funnel-web spider bites.

Red-back and other spiders

Red-back spider bites may be associated with excessive sweating. First aid for bites from all spiders other than funnel-webs involves easing local pain and swelling with an ice-pack and seeking medical assistance as quickly as possible. There is an antivenom available for red-back spider bites.

Ticks

It's important not to squeeze the tick as this may cause it to release more toxins. If you can, use very fine tweezers to grip *only* the barbed feeding tube and pull the tick out. Dabbing alcohol, insect repellent or pyrethrum-based spray onto the tick may cause it to die and fall out. If the tick is engorged it's advisable to have it removed by a medical practitioner, who will have the facilities available to deal with any reactions that may occur if the tick releases toxins during removal.

In the case of an allergic reaction, treat the symptoms with an asthma inhaler or antihistamine (page 185) and seek medical advice.

Centipedes and scorpions

A bite from these creatures, though painful, is very rarely dangerous. Ice or calamine lotion may ease the pain and if there is an allergic reaction, seek medical advice. (See also page 165.)

Bees and wasps

Bee stings should be removed immediately. Do not grasp the sting and pull, as this will only inject more venom. Using a sideways motion, scrape the sting out with a table knife or something similar. Wasps can withdraw their stings, so the foregoing doesn't apply. Apply an ice pack to ease the pain and, if faced with an allergic reaction, seek medical advice. (See also page 165.)

Ants and other insects

Apply an ice pack or calamine lotion to ease pain and swelling. If a severe allergic reaction occurs, seek medical advice. (See also page 165.)

MARINE FIRST AID
by Dr Carl Edmonds

Shark attack and other bite wounds

The principles of successful management of shark attack victims requires treatment for blood loss (page 163), immobilisation of the patient, and transport of medical support to the patient, not vice versa. It's also important to provide the patient with constant reassurance. First aid should be commenced immediately the patient is removed from the water, whether pulled onto a boat or surf-ski or carried to the shore. If the victim is wearing a wetsuit, don't remove it. It may help in reducing blood loss and damage to the internal organs.

Jellyfish and their kin

General

1. The victim should be rescued from the water, laid down and reassured.
2. Do not rub or damage tentacles still sticking to the patient.
3. Resuscitation (page 159) may be needed. Get medical help.
4. In a severe case of box jellyfish sting, douse liberally with vinegar.
5. Gently remove tentacles or nematocysts if they are still adhering to the skin, preferably using tweezers or gloves.
6. Local applications (described below) may help relieve pain.

Local applications

The recommendations as to which local applications to use are still contentious. Years ago, alcohol was thought to reduce further damage but recent surveys suggest that it's of no value in either prevention or treatment, and may in fact actively trigger the discharge of some nematocysts. Similarly, widely advertised over-the-counter remedies are of little value.

Calamine lotion has also been recommended in the past, as have washing blue, lime juice, ammonia, baking soda and meat tenderiser, but none of these are currently used.

Any treatment that works for superficial burns – sunburn sprays for example – will also work to some degree against mild cnidarian injuries. Ointment containing a local anaesthetic is partially effective in reducing pain and steroid ointment may be used later if itching becomes a problem. Ice packs give some relief, as may any preparation that cools by evaporation. For the more common stings, there are indications that certain common substances including stale wine and cola drinks may be of value. With severe stings, however, none of these remedies are adequate.

Copious dousing with vinegar (mild acetic acid) is an old treatment that has recently been revived. It reduces the number of nematocyst discharges from the more serious box jellyfish stings but doesn't relieve the pain – and it may actually cause other jellyfish species, including *Cyanea* (page 118) and the Portuguese man-o'-war (page 109), to discharge more nematocysts.

Box jellyfish

1. Rescue the victim from the water to prevent drowning.
2. The ABC of first aid – Airway maintenance, Breathing support and Circulation maintenance, as described on page 159 – may be needed.

3. Apply copious amounts of ordinary household vinegar to the tentacles for 30 seconds or more, before gently removing them from the victim's skin. The tentacles can't sting effectively through the thick skin of the palms of the hands and fingers so tentacle removal is safer for the rescuer than it sounds. It's important not to rub or damage the tentacles as this will encourage them to inject further venom into the victim.
4. Alcohol application is no longer advised, as there is some evidence that this may cause the discharge of further venom into the victim.
5. Some authorities have suggested that the application of pressure-immobilisation (page 181) may be of benefit.
6. The cause of death from box jellyfish sting may be respiratory failure. However, this danger may pass if the victim is kept alive by EAR or other artificial ventilation during this period. The victim should be transported to hospital urgently.
7. An antivenom against box jellyfish stings developed by CSL neutralises the venom present in the victim's body and should be used in severe cases or where significant local scarring is threatened. It may not be effective against other "sea wasp" species.

Fish stings

General
1. The patient's state may be far more serious than it first appears. S/he should be laid down and reassured.
2. If the fish spine or pieces of tissue are present, they should be gently extracted. Leaving the wound to bleed a little may help remove some of the venom.
3. Remove surface venom by washing the area with water.
4. Rest the affected limb in an elevated position.
5. Immerse the wound in hot (up to 45°C) water for 30–90 minutes, or until the pain diminishes (see below).
6. When heat treatment is no longer required, wash and clean the wound with antiseptic.
7. Following pain relief, the limb should be immobilised in an elevated position and covered with a clean dressing.
8. Ligatures, tourniquets and pressure bandages shouldn't be used as they may cause further injury by restricting circulation.

Heat treatment

To provide heat treatment, you may need to improvise. Hot fluids from car radiators or picnic thermoses can be diluted to the right temperature – with sea water if necessary. If a thermometer isn't handy, unaffected skin should be immersed first, to gauge the water temperature and prevent scalding. The duration of the hot-water immersion will depend on the symptoms. In a series of recorded fish stingings, 84 per cent were alleviated merely by the application of hot water.

If there is only a little water available, the limb can be enclosed in a plastic bag, which can then be partially filled with hot fluid, or used as a "hot pack". Hot packs are particularly useful when it isn't possible to immerse the wound. If hot liquid isn't available, hot stones or sand can also be effective.

WARNING: One unfortunate fisherman had to have the top of his finger removed after it was anaesthetised then immersed in very hot water. Unable to feel the pain, his finger was so severely scalded that it required amputation.

Stonefish – additional treatment

1. If the patient loses consciousness, external heart massage and mouth-to-mouth resuscitation (page 159) may be required for many hours; do not cease until death is confirmed.
2. Stonefish antivenom is now available and its use may be required in severe cases.

Stingray

Damage from the spine may cause death from either envenomation, blood loss or physical trauma, such as the penetration of the abdomen or major organs such as the lungs and heart. These require additional first-aid and surgical treatments depending on the area affected (page 163).

Other marine creatures

Blue-ringed octopus

Without paralysis:
1. Wash the toxin from the wound.
2. Apply a pressure bandage (page 181) and immobilise the limb or bite site.

3. Rest the patient, preferably lying on his/her side. Do not leave him/her unattended.
4. Send for medical assistance.
5. Reassure the patient.

With paralysis:

1. Attend to the airway, perform mouth-to-mouth resuscitation and, if necessary, external cardiac massage (page 159).
2. Artificial respiration must be continued until recovery (6–12 hours) because of the respiratory muscle paralysis. Otherwise treat as above.

Cone shell

Without paralysis:

1. Apply a pressure bandage (page 181) and immobilise the limb or sting site.
2. Rest the patient, but do not leave him/her unattended.
3. Summon medical assistance.
4. Give reassurance.

With paralysis:

1. The application of a pressure bandage and immobilisation should delay the spread of venom from the wound, although clinical case reports have yet to confirm this.
2. The ABC resuscitative measures (page 159) should keep the patient alive until the respiratory paralysis has worn off. This may involve many hours of artificial respiration.

Sea-snakes

1. The application of a pressure bandage (page 181) should delay symptoms until medical assistance, resuscitation facilities and antivenom can be acquired.
2. ABC first-aid measures should be instituted where necessary (page 159).
3. Mouth-to-mouth resuscitation is required in cases of paralysis.
4. The victim should be taken to hospital as rapidly as possible.
5. Serious cases of envenomation should be treated with sea-snake antivenom.

When recovery occurs – within 1–2 days of envenomation – it's rapid and complete.

Sea urchin

The long spines tend to break easily and need to be removed vertically, without any horizontal movement. Surgical removal may be necessary, especially if symptoms are severe or persistent; a local anaesthetic may be required. Drawing-pastes such as magnesium sulphate have been used successfully as have old snakebite suction cups. The application of heat has provided relief for some victims during the early stages.

One emergency technique that seems to work, as bizarre as it may seem, is to apply extra trauma to break up the spines within the tissue by hitting the area of the wound with a flat or smooth object – a sandshoe, for example. This method may be especially useful in remote areas where medical assistance is unavailable.

Movement of the limb is also encouraged as activity appears to be more beneficial than rest and immobilisation; otherwise, the limb tends to swell and become more painful. The spine fragments are eventually absorbed.

Sponge

The only adequate treatment is prevention: use gloves when handling sponges and don't touch anything that has been in contact with a sponge. The use of alcohol, lotions or hot water will usually aggravate the condition. Local application of a cooling lotion, such as calamine, may be of some value, but in general, treatment of the skin lesion has met with very limited success.

Segmented worms

1. Some bristles can be removed by applying the sticky surface of adhesive tape or sticking plaster to the area and ripping it off, together with the bristles. Individual bristles can be removed with surgical forceps, assisted by magnification. Rubbing the area with sand will also remove some bristles.
2. Bites should be washed with salt water, sodium bicarbonate or antiseptic.
3. Cooling lotions or local anaesthetics can be used and antibiotic ointment applied.
4. Bed rest, medical aid and resuscitation may be necessary.

Part   I I I

MEDICAL FIRST AID AND MORE ADVANCED TREATMENTS
by Dr Carl Edmonds

This section provides specific emergency first-aid information, as well as references to allergic reactions and anaesthesia. It includes some technical terms that won't be recognised by all readers as this material is intended primarily for the medical attendants who take over the first-aid management of a patient. In the event of an injury from one of the creatures described here, the book should accompany the patient and be made available to the treating doctor or paramedic.

TOURNIQUETS, LIGATURES AND PRESSURE BANDAGES

Tourniquets are used to stop severe bleeding from wounds caused by trauma such as a shark attack. They work by stopping the arterial blood flow into limbs, at the same time stopping venous blood flow out of the limb. They are of necessity very tight and painful.

Ligatures, or venous tourniquets, were once used to delay the absorption and transport of venom into the systemic circulation, and to some extent to assist the removal of venom by promoting bleeding. They were used to stop the venous blood and some lymph flow from the limbs, but weren't tight enough to impede arterial blood flow. They may have been useful in delaying the effects of venom while medical assistance was obtained.

Any flexible piece of material of a suitable length and width, a belt, necktie or strong handkerchief for example, can be used as a tourniquet or ligature. Pressure can be applied by wide straps, clothing, air splints and other materials.

Because venom initially moves through the lymphatic system rather than the blood, pressure bandages with immobilisation have superseded ligatures in the treatment of envenomation. The pressure, applied over a wide area where the venom has infiltrated, compresses the lymphatic drainage vessels, reducing or blocking the movement of venom into the bloodstream until the pressure is removed.

Tourniquets

Tourniquets are used to stop severe bleeding from a limb where other methods, such as the application of pressure with a large pad and/or bandage, are inadequate. In an emergency a tourniquet can be made from a belt, or items of clothing torn into strips. However, avoid using shoelaces or twine as these can cut into the flesh.

1. Lie the patient down with the limb elevated. Tie a piece of the material around the limb, over clothing or padding to avoid pinching the skin.
2. Tie the tourniquet around the upper part of the limb between the wound and the body. Pass a stick or rod through the knot.
3. Using the stick as a lever, turn it to tighten the tourniquet until the bleeding stops, after which no further tightening is necessary.
4. Tie a second piece of material around the limb near the tourniquet and secure the end of the stick to prevent it unwinding.
5. Take note of the time the tourniquet was applied.

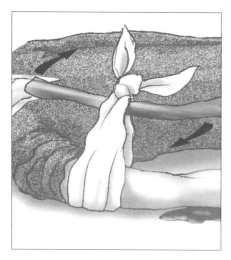 

6. Loosen the tourniquet after 20 minutes. If it needs to be reapplied it must be loosened every 20 minutes thereafter. If bleeding doesn't resume after the tourniquet is loosened the blood has probably begun to clot. Leave the loosened tourniquet in place, ready to be tightened should the need arise.
7. The injured limb and tourniquet should be left uncovered and kept under continuous observation in case bleeding recommences. The injury may benefit from being exposed to the cold.

If the injury is to a part of the body where a tourniquet can't be applied, fold clothing or towels and press them firmly on the wound. If it's necessary to add more padding, place it over that previously applied.

There are grave dangers associated with the use of tourniquets and they should only be applied as a lifesaving measure – for example to stop bleeding of a severed main artery or when a limb has been torn off. The area beyond the tourniquet is deprived of its blood supply and if the tourniquet is left on for too long, it will become gangrenous and amputation will be unavoidable.

Tourniquets can cause damage to underlying tissue such as nerves, resulting in an impaired sensation of touch, numbness, tingling and paralysis. Tourniquets are always painful, local bruising is inevitable, and these may both contribute towards the degree of shock.

If the tourniquet is applied too loosely it will act as a ligature and will only stop the venous blood flow from the limb back to the heart. Arterial blood will still be flowing and because of the ligature effect, blood loss will actually be increased.

Pressure bandage with immobilisation

Research performed at the CSL has had a direct bearing on the value of ligatures, tourniquets and other forms of first-aid treatment against injected venoms. Investigations were performed to determine the effects that these devices had on the quantity of venom present in the plasma of animals that were injected with venom.

CSL's results suggested that the application of a firm crepe bandage (or a localised pressure pad) and splint, is an excellent method of retarding the absorption of venom. This technique seems as effective as an arterial tourniquet in the short-term, but it's far more practical because of the

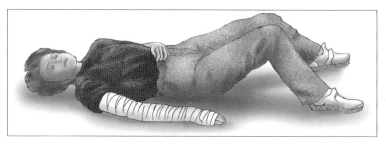

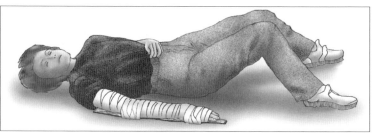

comfort, the greatly reduced likelihood of localised ischaemia or gangrene and the extended duration over which it can be applied. The delay in venom absorption allows time for antivenom to be acquired and used.

Because of the delay in venom absorption, the pressure-immobilisation method should even be applied to severely envenomated patients who are found late. It should also be reapplied if the patient becomes critically ill on removal of the bandage. Application of the bandage increases the amount of time available to obtain antivenom to neutralise the venom, and may also reduce the antivenom requirement.

Dr Julian White has recommended that this technique be used in the treatment of all types of Australian snakebite (page 168), suspected funnel-web spider bites, and certain marine stings, such as those of the blue-ringed octopus and cone shell. He has also suggested that it could be used for box jellyfish stings, but this is more contentious and shouldn't replace the vinegar treatment (page 174).

He also suggests that the technique isn't appropriate for bites from the red-back or other spiders, scorpions, centipedes or stings from venomous fish. As a rule of thumb, any sting that results in very severe swelling and inflammation probably isn't as suitable for pressure-immobilisation as those in which the venom is absorbed rapidly through the lymphatic system. It's also worth noting that the pressure-immobilisation method isn't necessarily suitable for treatment of snakebite in countries other than Australia.

ALLERGIES, ANAPHYLAXIS AND ANAESTHESIA

Allergy and anaphylaxis

Stings from some animals or insects, or even mere contact with them, can produce an allergic or anaphylactic response. In some cases, such as an allergic reaction to a bee sting, this can be far more serious than the envenomation from the sting itself. The victim could well survive the envenomation, but succumb to the anaphylaxis. Allergy can also be produced in response to an antivenom.

If the victim is already sensitised to a venom (or a similar protein), the allergy or anaphylaxis can come on very rapidly, within minutes of the sting or bite. Alternatively, if the victim wasn't previously sensitive to the venom but develops the sensitivity following the sting, then the allergy or anaphylaxis may be delayed for up to two weeks.

Acute anaphylaxis is a severe, sometimes fatal, allergic reaction to a substance to which the victim is hypersensitive. In the most extreme cases, it develops within seconds or minutes of exposure and death may follow within 10 minutes. Patients frequently experience mild generalised itchiness, slight tightness of the chest, tingling of the lips, a tickle in the throat, palate or around the neck, agitation and/or restlessness.

The anaphylaxis syndrome may resolve within a few minutes of treatment or may persist for many hours despite treatment. Vascular (blood vessel) collapse is a prominent component of this syndrome and may occur alone, without involvement of other systems. Sometimes symptoms recur about 4–6 hours after apparent resolution of the syndrome, particularly when adrenaline is used as the sole form of treatment. Most deaths outside hospital occur within 10 minutes of exposure, but even with treatment the patient may die within the first two hours. The longer treatment is delayed, the more refractory becomes the syndrome.

Allergy is a systemic reaction affecting several organs. The skin is frequently involved and the patient complains of itching, erythema (reddening of the skin or rash) or urticarial reactions, similar to hives. Bronchospasm – similar to asthma – is common. The patient may also complain of cough, stridor (wheezing), dyspnoea (laboured breathing), tightness of the chest and pain, and may be cyanosed (have a blue tinge to lips and skin) from respiratory obstruction as well as bronchospasm. Symptoms involving the gastrointestinal tract may include cramps, diarrhoea and sometimes vomiting. Women may also experience lower abdominal pain due to uterine cramps.

Hives is by far the most common allergic reaction, asthma is less common, and serious anaphylaxis relatively uncommon. Management of anaphylaxis demands urgent measures.

In a number of cases, both local and general allergies have developed following a sting. These can be severe and confusing to the patient and therapist, as was the case with the injury sustained by a fisherman stung by a jellyfish. The wound rapidly cleared up, but the skin reaction was moderately severe and caused great discomfort for many years whenever the victim exposed himself to the same ocean conditions at the same time of the year. Local remedies were not particularly effective; however, it was discovered that the reaction could be averted if steroids were taken for a few days soon after exposure. Old fishermen's stories of wounds recurring at the same time each year for seven years may be explained by this mechanism.

Another patient developed severe and generalised hives approximately one week after being bitten by a blue-ringed octopus, well after he had recovered from the initial envenomation.

Many people experience allergic reactions when they come into contact with or simply get close to fish, animals or insects. In these cases, there will often be an asthma-type reaction.

Clinical features

Milder cases of allergy may only involve the skin, with the development of red, weal-like, itchy patches – the equivalent of hives.

There may be evidence of abdominal cramps, diarrhoea and sometimes vomiting – especially when protein is ingested. Women may experience low-abdominal pain associated with spasms of the uterine muscle.

If the lungs are affected, causing increased secretion from the airways and bronchospasm, the patient may develop a type of asthma with severe breathlessness, stridor, tightness or pain in the chest, and may have evidence of respiratory obstruction, such as cyanosis.

In the most severe form – acute anaphylaxis – the main syndrome develops because the blood vessels are affected, causing a drop in blood pressure, rapid pulse, loss of consciousness (especially when standing) and possibly death.

In infants there is a tendency for severe respiratory anaphylactic symptoms. Acute collapse, syncope (fainting), respiratory depression, a stunned, drowsy appearance or abdominal distension – with or without bile-stained vomiting – may occur alone or in any combination. Even the milder cases may appear drowsy, with abdominal distension and vomiting.

In children many of the features of anaphylaxis are similar to those seen in adults and described above.

Although the syndrome can resolve within a few hours, it isn't uncommon for it to last longer – especially if the skin is affected. The respiratory and anaphylaxis symptoms tend to be more acute, dangerous and of a shorter duration. Deaths may occur within 10 minutes of exposure, although any patient who survives more than the first few hours should be reasonably safe – assuming adequate treatment has been given. The longer treatment is delayed, the more difficult the syndrome is to treat.

➕ **For basic first aid see page 165.**

Medical first aid for allergy and anaphylaxis

Outside the hospital environment the medical practitioner may find the following very useful:

1. Adrenaline 1/1000 for intramuscular injection; corticosteroids and antihistamines for parenteral administration.
2. Facilities for establishing an intravenous line, such as a drip set and intravenous saline.
3. The capacity to perform artificial ventilation and cardiopulmonary resuscitation (page 158).
4. Oxygen.

Urticaria (hives)

Antihistamines, orally or systematically, may be of value.

Asthma

Administer adrenaline as described below. Other anti-asthma medications may be of value, such as salbutamol (e.g. Ventolin) or the steroid sprays (e.g. Becotide), as these may relieve the asthma and may also be absorbed.

Anaphylaxis

1. Stop exposure to, or administration of, the causal agent. Consider inducing vomiting or gastric lavage if the allergic material has recently been ingested and if the patient is fully conscious and has laryngeal reflex.
2. Place the patient in a recumbent position, with the lower extremities elevated.
3. Restore ventilation and circulation:
4. Give adrenaline 1:1000, 0.3–0.5 ml intramuscularly for adults or 0.01 ml/kg for children. Repeat in five minutes if necessary.
5. Establish an intravenous line. To expand blood volume if the patient is in shock, give colloid solution such as 10% SPPS plus 5% dextrose, or large volumes of electrolyte solutions if colloids are unavailable.
6. If the patient doesn't respond to intramuscular adrenaline, or if peripheral circulation is poor and shock is severe, give adrenaline intravenously in a dose of 5 ml 1:10,000 adrenaline or 0.5 ml 1:1000, diluted in 10 ml normal saline over 10 minutes. In the presence of venous or arterial stasis, intracardiac injection may be necessary. Give external cardiac massage if the patient has no pulse.
7. Give oxygen 100%. Assist ventilation (bag and mask, intubation or even tracheotomy as necessary).
8. Give corticosteroids intravenously, for example, hydrocortisone 200 mg. While steroids aren't helpful for the immediate acute situation, they may assist in preventing protracted anaphylaxis, or a relapse.
9. Give antihistamines (promethazine 25 mg or diphenhydramine 50 mg intramuscularly or intravenously).
10. If there is severe bronchospasm, administer aerosolised bronchodilators and/or aminophylline 3–6 mg/kg intravenously over 10 minutes followed by 0.5–0.9 mg/kg every hour if required.

Supportive treatment

1. Monitor vital signs frequently and maintain patient under medical observation for at least four hours.
2. Give reassurance. Avoid heat, exercise and alcohol.
3. Avoid hypotensive and vasodilating drugs. Vasopressor drugs are rarely indicated, but may be if there has been no response to adequate colloids and adrenaline.

Follow-up treatment

1. Determine the cause. Provide identification bracelet (Medic Alert) and advise regarding precautions to prevent recurrence.
2. Provide drug protection if exposure is unavoidable, for example, antihistamines or steroids.

Anaesthesia

The initial methods for obtaining effective pain relief for bites and stings are physical applications, including both heat and cold compresses. The use of heat, especially for fish stings and some other marine animal envenomations, is described on page 176. Cold or ice packs may be of value in envenomations that produce inflammation such as jellyfish stings, spider bites, and scorpion and centipede stings. When these are inadequate, local anaesthesia may be used in the form of topical anaesthesia (contact sprays, ointments or creams) or local infiltration (injection into tissues).

These easy and safe techniques are often all that's required. Regional block and general anaesthesia are more difficult and risky. They are rarely needed and require knowledge and expertise in the field of anaesthesia, and should only be undertaken where the measures described above are inadequate.

Drugs

There is a wide range of local anaesthetic drugs and preparations available. All may produce central nervous system toxicity (convulsions) if injected intravascularly or if an overdose is administered. Except perhaps in regional block, plain solutions (that is, containing no adrenaline) should be used, as in many stings there are already ischaemic effects from the venom.

Lignocaine (trade name Xylocaine)

This is the most widely available drug and may be used for topical, infiltration or regional anaesthesia. It has a rapid onset of action and a duration of approximately 60–120 minutes. A 0.5% solution is suitable for infiltration, 1.0–1.5% for regional block. Creams, ointments and jelly preparations usually contain about 4–5% weight for weight. Aerosols deliver approximately 10 mg per puff.

Bupivacaine (trade name Marcain)

This is suitable for infiltration (0.25%) or regional block (0.25–0.5%) anaesthesia because of its much longer duration of action (up to 12 hours in the case of brachial block). It's available in 0.25–0.5% solutions with or without adrenaline.

Cocaine

In 4% solution cocaine is suitable for stings to the eye where corneal anaesthesia is needed.

ADMINISTRATION

Topical application

Local anaesthetic preparations may be applied to areas permitting penetration of the agent. Such areas are mucous membranes, open wounds, or areas in which skin has been damaged. Local anaesthetics will not readily penetrate intact skin. They may be useful when superficial skin inflammation has developed, with hydroid, Portuguese man-o'-war or jimble stings, for example.

Many anti-burn or soothing preparations are available, sometimes in the form of aerosol sprays, and are effective in the less serious stings. Commercial preparations such as Stingose, Stop-itch, and Instant Aid may be useful.

Local infiltration

This involves the direct injection by a physician or a trained paramedic of the anaesthetic agent into the tissues involved. Conventional techniques include adequate asepsis, injection of the solution from healthy tissues towards injured tissues, avoidance of significant intravascular injection by keeping the needle moving, and complete encircling of the lesion by the agent. This method is especially valuable with very painful injuries and fish stings. Adrenaline should not be added in the treatment of stings, as many venoms are already vasoconstrictive in their effect.

GLOSSARY

Abdomen The rear body division of an insect or arachnid.

Allergy A physical hypersensitivity to a particular substance.

Anal scale The enlarged ventral scale on the anterior margin of the vent (anus).

Anaphylaxis A severe allergic reaction.

Anterior Situated closer to the front; opposite of posterior.

Anticoagulant Substance that promotes bleeding by blocking the clotting process.

Arachnid Member of the class Arachnida. Includes spiders, ticks, scorpions and mites.

Arboreal Living primarily in trees.

Arthropod Invertebrate animal with a hard exoskeleton. Includes insects, spiders and crustaceans.

Bell The dome-shaped body of a jellyfish.

Carapace The dorsal part of an animal's protective shell. In spiders refers to the dorsal plate of the cephalothorax.

Cardiac arrest When the heart stops beating.

Carnivorous Feeding on animals.

Carotid Either of the two large arteries, one on each side of the neck, carrying blood to the head.

Caudal Relating to the tail.

Cephalothorax In spiders the anterior body division made up of the head and thorax.

Chelicerae The jaws of spiders, consisting of a fang and a fang base.

Class In biological classification the major subdivision of a phylum; contains one or more orders.

Cloaca The chamber into which the reproductive, intestinal and urinary ducts open in reptiles, amphibians, monotremes, marsupials and birds.

Cnidarian Member of the phylum Cnidaria. Includes jellyfish, sea anemones, corals, fire corals and stinging hydroids.

Coelenterate Name previously given to members of the phylum Cnidaria.

CPR CardioPulmonary Resuscitation.

Crustacean Member of the phylum Crustacea. Includes crabs, lobsters and shrimps.

Cyanosis Blueness of the skin due to a lack of oxygen in the blood.

Detritus Broken up and decaying organic matter.

Distribution The area in which a species occurs.

Diurnal Active by day.

Dorsal Pertaining to the upper surface.

DRABC First-aid action plan: **D**anger, **R**esponse, **A**irway, **B**reathing, **C**irculation.

Dry bite A venomous-snake bite where no venom is injected.

EAR **E**xpired **A**ir **R**esuscitation; "mouth-to-mouth".

Echinoderm Member of the phylum Echinodermata. Includes sea urchins and starfish.

Ectothermic Deriving body heat from external sources; cold-blooded.

Endemic Found only in a particular region.

Endothermic Producing body heat internally; warm-blooded.

Envenomation The injection of venom.

Exoskeleton The tough outer skeleton of arthropods such as insects, spiders, centipedes and crustaceans.

Family In biological classification the major subdivision of an order; contains one or more genera.

Frontal scale The large dorsal scale between the eyes of most snakes.

Genus (plural Genera) In biological classification the major subdivision of a family; contains one or more species.

Habitat An area providing the physical and biological conditions required for a particular species.

Keeled Bearing a raised ridge; usually refers to reptile scales.

Labial scale Scale on a reptile's upper or lower lip.

Lateral Pertaining to the sides.

Loreal scale The scale lying on the side of a snake's snout between the nasal and preocular scales.

Mandible Main chewing mouthparts of insects.

Moult To shed the outer skin or exoskeleton during growth.

MYA Million Years Ago.

Myolysis Muscle destruction.

Myotoxin Toxin that destroys muscle cells.

Nasal scale The scale on a reptile's snout enclosing or bordering the nostril.

Necrosis Death of an area of tissue.

Nematocyst Stinging cell of jellyfish and their kin.

Neurotoxin Toxin that affects the nervous system.

Nocturnal Active by night.

Order In biological classification the major subdivision of a class; contains one or more families.

Ovipositor Egg-laying organ in insects. Modified to form a sting in some wasps and ants.

Pedicellariae Pincer-like structures on the surface of echinoderms such as sea urchins.

Phylum (plural Phyla) The second-highest category of biological classification; subdivision of kingdom; contains one or more classes.

Polyp The sedentary form of cnidarian. Includes sea anemones and individual members of cnidarian colonies such as corals.

Posterior Towards the hind end; opposite of anterior.

Preocular scale The scale adjacent to the eye anteriorly.

Procoagulant Toxin that destroys the blood-clotting protein.

Rugose Wrinkled, ridged or uneven.

Sedentary Moving only rarely.

Species Group of animals sharing common characteristics and capable of breeding with one another to produce fertile offspring; the basic category of biological classification; subdivision of genus.

Spinneret Short tube-like organ at the posterior end of a spider's abdomen that produces silk.

Subcaudal scale A scale underneath the tail posterior to the anal scale.

Subspecies A subdivision of a species consisting of individuals with characteristics that distinguish them from others of the same species.

Syncope Brief loss of consciousness.

Terrestrial Living on the ground.

Thorax The middle body section in insects and some other arthropods to which the limbs are attached.

Toxin Any poisonous substance derived from a plant or animal; the component of a venom that causes ill effects.

Trichobothria The sensory hairs on the limbs of spiders.

Venom Poisonous substance produced by an animal.

Vent The external opening of the cloaca.

Ventral Pertaining to the underside.

INDEX

Page numbers in *italics* indicate photographs, but where a reference appears in both text and photograph on the same page, it appears in roman type only. Page references for first aid are in **bold** type.